Cry
Downriver

Cry Downriver

JOHN PEPPER

QUARTET

First published in 2011 by Quartet Books Limited
A member of the Namara Group
27 Goodge Street, London W1T 2LD

Copyright © John Pepper 2011

The right of John Pepper to be identified as the author
of this work has been asserted by him in accordance with
the Copyright, Designs and Patents Act 1988

A catalogue record for this book is available from the British Library

ISBN   978 0 7043 7208 5

Typeset in Helvetica by Antony Gray
Printed and bound in Great Britain by
T J International Ltd, Padstow, Cornwall

'A world of beauty and compassion
in spite of everything'

Jonathan Wittenberg
The Silence of Dark Water

Dearest Ruth,

Cannot imagine what you must have been thinking and feeling, at the wheel of your car still, the interior light on, as you sailed down the middle of the river in the dark. A witness said you looked 'remarkably calm'. Or was the truth of it you were paralysed with disbelief? Terror?

The old Ford, tumbling, gathering speed down deepening pools, starts to ship water. You clamber to get hold of Sara in the back. You know she's as frightened of water as you are, and doesn't swim. But the dog, waterlogged, thrashing, is drowning already. You're going to drown as well unless . . .

Opening the door, if you could, would most likely sink you, straight. The electrics, however, are working still. You get your window down and somehow, at some point, with the energy of endgame, and Sara gone, you stuff yourself through. You strike out for – what, though? All around you is black flood, black night. Pelting rain. You haven't a chance. The swollen river gathers you up and pours you away.

Then what? Could be, at the last, it was sweet surrender? I hope so.

Haunted I am, the day after, your half-naked body having just been fished out seven long miles downstream, by your deep, dark fear; in your own words, of 'deep, dark water where I can't see the bottom'. You used to say it had stalked you all your life. Convinced in every cell of your being of the reality of reincarnation, you always declared you had drowned in your life before this one.

Now *this*.

D'you remember only last month when we were wandering

around the Greek islands, so happy the pair of us, how I'd tease you about your never venturing into even the translucent blue waters of the Aegean above your thighs? 'Come on, I'll swim alongside you,' I'd called to you on one occasion, laughing. 'You'll be perfectly safe, Ruth. I promise, you won't drown!'

But no, couldn't get you to swim out, could I? So careful you were.

Which is why this afternoon after your death I'm angry not only with the river – have come straight here, hurling stones and invective at the thing – I am also pretty mad, my love, at you. Because you died, I'm sure of it, through carelessness. You'd been warned about the road by the river just half an hour before you perished, your neighbour Doug Allen having pointed out how heavy the rain had been that afternoon and how dangerous Flood Lane (yes, Flood Lane as you knew the locals used to call it) might be that night. He'd tried to stop you going hadn't he, saying 'Leave it till morning, Ruth.' But you'd said 'No', and you were off; you'd the animals to feed at the farm, you'd be all right. 'Get any problems,' Doug had pleaded, 'just give me a ring and I'll come and lend you a hand.'

I suspect your mind was on other things. The arrival next morning of your niece Becca maybe, and pondering the cake or casserole you might put together for her that evening when you got to Jackie's, where you were caretaking while she was abroad. Something like that. Had your mind been on the road and the rain, surely you'd have seen the spate upfront? And, perhaps, backed off in time?

Whatever. Suddenly your car was afloat, sweeping in a circle into the middle of the river then, bonnet forward, away you went.

When I came to see you this week in the chapel of rest, even with the undertaker's care and cosmetics it was obvious you'd been knocked black and blue. The man said he was sorry, he'd done his best. And there was the brass epitaph at the side, on the lid of your coffin: 'Fell Asleep'. Which, in taking your eye off your driving for even a paltry few seconds, daydreaming, I believe you did, in effect, even before you drowned.

In tears, I stroked your hair and touched your marble cheek, muttered 'You were a silly sod, Ruth' – never did stand on ceremony did we? – told you I would love you always, and laid one rose across your heart.

ARE YOU TRYING to tell me you're OK? The afternoon of my paddy with the river, I am then walking, weeping, through the streets of your town. Two women are standing on the pavement talking about the accident. As I pass I call out, 'Ruth France was my dearest friend.'

One of the women asks, 'Was that the name of the lady who died? Ohmygod! *My* name's Ruth France too.' True. It was the namesake in the town whom you knew.

A few days later, shortly before I'd got to see you at the chapel of rest, a letter landed on my doormat. My heart quickened with joy. It was from you. You *weren't* dead. In some form or other, you were alive even now. The games grief plays . . . I tore the letter open, only to discover it wasn't from you of course, it was from a former student of mine. But she'd known you, and her handwriting on the envelope was identical more or less to your own.

Then two other friends of yours reported they were walking by the river at the spot where your body had washed up a few days earlier, and suddenly one turned and jumped. There on the earth by her feet was your name, 'Ruth', beautifully woven in the bronze of autumn leaves.

You did, you had that sort of effect on people.

In my dreams I hear you calling me. I awake, startled, coated in sweat. Yet it is not your voice, my name; it is only the wind, the soft night hum of the city. The mournful ambient music of loneliness, of abject loss.

NOT YET FOUR O'CLOCK in the morning, hours short of dawn, I get up and write to you under the light of one small lamp. My page wrinkles with tears. I tear it up and shuffle around the gloaming touching things to try to maintain some semblance of order in the storm, stop me going mad. I cling to symmetry. Cushions lined up; one, two, three. On the wall, a tilted painting corrected. A paperclip set at a right-angle to the edge of my desk.

One disturbed night a few weeks ago, before you vanished, I was sitting here at my window overlooking the shimmering city when a large white owl had alighted on the bollard in the street immediately below me, then gone hunting, vision from another world in lamplight, gliding across the long wild grass beyond.

Now I long for it to return, that it might be a messenger bearing meanings, something; gifts from you. But nothing stirs. The night city bares its sulphur-yellow fangs back at me. There is nowhere to go. No release. No hope. You're dead and gone. Forever? I don't know. I know nothing at all.

Rob, Rachel and baby Anya have flown back from Kenya. I meet Rob in your high street where we sit over coffee in a daze. I take him down to the river where his mother went in, pointing to the breach in the trees at the side where the flood, after sweeping down the lane, re-entered the race, taking your car with it. The opening was cut by farmers gathering stones from the riverbed for walls and tracks. If it hadn't been there your wheels would have snaffled in the shrubbery on the river's edge and you'd have been saved. That gap killed you. Absurdly, I feel like screaming at the farmers too. I take Rob to the old Sun pub in the village up the road and we have a couple of slow pints by the fire instead.

Your funeral is plain, as befits a onetime-upstanding Methodist gal. The boys speak of you with choked sobs and much love. At your life's end, Ruth, you get standing-room-only and, in a celebration of that life afterwards, there's a book of tributes to you being handwritten by people in a queue. Then, on the other side of the room, I see you, clear as yesterday. I beeline across and hug you.

It's your sister Tricia – (painful) photocopy of you – from whom you had alas been estranged for so many years and I've not seen for, what, fifteen? I tell her, whatever the differences which had divided you, 'Ruth loved you.' You did, a lot, I know. And sadly.

Afterwards, night beyond night, wide-eyed, I still peer out for the owl.

I TRY to deal with my grief by writing about you in the papers: 'In all my life as a counsellor and writer, I have never encountered an individual as warm-hearted and empathetic.'

And: 'Her relentless giving to others came at a price to her health, yet she overcame depressions and demons with great insight. Deeply spiritual, she was a beautiful soul, with a deliciously wicked sense of humour. Her son Chris once described her as "the best kind of human being it is possible to be". His brother Rob said she was "a star".'

'A beautiful woman, and her life a radiant one,' I went on else-where. 'Once my partner too, she remained my spiritual friend, unendingly beloved.'

I have to go on writing, on and on. In the bleak midwinter, I cannot let you go. Stay with me till springtime when I shall return to 'our' island in the sun where I'll lay wild flowers in memory of you in the clear turquoise waters, which in the end you *did* enjoy, paddling around on your bum In the shallows (just a few safe inches of briny), so much at peace. I remember how we talked, daftly, of going to live on that minute, unspoiled piece of the archipelago and do nothing there but 'be'. 'Being' rather than 'doing', 'going', 'getting' and 'having' the story, wasn't it, of both our lives now. *Being real.*

IT'S FUNNY, I don't think many people had a clear idea of the kind of love we'd crafted. Defied easy classification, didn't it? Our relationship, I recall, flummoxed even your great friend Jackie who did so much to shelter you from the storms of your later life and whose farm it was you were tending when you died. 'I don't understand it,' she'd told you, hadn't she? When I described you as 'my dearest companion' in a couple of the obituaries I wrote I had one news editor, then an obits sub, ring to ask, 'What exactly *was* your relationship?' The phrase 'dearest companion' seemed to bamboozle many. A third hack couldn't get his head round my describing you as my 'spiritual sister'. I think he got to worrying about things like incest, maybe. What everyone wanted to know of course was, 'Were you in a sexual relationship or weren't you?' No, we weren't. Our sex life, essentially, had ended ages back hadn't it? What we were trying to do was love each other beyond sex, measure or need. The world has no ready 'box' today for those who aren't in a sexual relationship but are a good deal more than 'friends', does it? Those who are wed not in law or custom but in spirit, as we were – brother and sister, at the close, in something at least approximating the peace *and* the love 'that passeth understanding'?

'Soulmates' would be the obvious description for our pairing I suppose, but the word is invariably trotted out as a top-up to 'partner' in the conventional sense – and in light of our rollercoaster history we'd have had some difficulty describing ourselves as 'partners' in the first place, wouldn't we?

Anyway. Ruth, in Hebrew, according to my Funk & Wagnalls, interprets as 'companion'. That'll do for me.

So, what exactly did happen to you in those last few hours of your life, Ruth? Let's wind back, slowly, shall we . . .

THE UNSUSPECTING MORNING had been a glad one. We'd had a lazy breakfast at the farm then, a little later, gone to have some quiet time at the communal meditation centre in the village. There'd been only the two of us, silent as starlight, in the empty room. That I'd taught you to meditate so many years before, from day one of our meeting, and that you'd kept up, well, some practice through all those that followed had always chuffed me. Side by side, wasn't it, a 'journey through space'. For both of us too, descending into the pits of our beings, an odyssey through storms, bringing to awareness the stories of our unconscious selves, our 'dark', our shadows. That morning, however, so many miles and awakenings down the line, there is only the peace of the valley, inside and out.

And so our life together begins and ends, exactly, with meditation. The meditation I liked to describe as the quest in our two lives for a 'love worthy of its name'.

We had a bite for lunch and said our goodbyes till the weekend, when I'd be coming back to be with you again at the farm. You'd a massage client awaiting you at your home and I had to get back to my counselling work, restarting in the city the next day. There'd been a lot of rain, the last couple. We motored down Jackie's drive in our separate cars. At the bottom you turned right and I was surprised. You'd always told me to turn left, go round and up into the village and avoid the lane skirting the beck to the right when we'd had bad weather. The lane's notorious for flooding. There've been incidents with people getting stuck and having to abandon their vehicles smartish, or climb on their roofs. But if you turn left, although you might run into floodwaters and have a problem getting through, you don't face the possibility of a *river* slewing over the road.

I shrugged and followed you, thinking 'Well if there's water upfront she'll soon find out for the pair of us and if necessary we can backtrack.' Actually the river was alright; it was quite a bit lower than the road, still the proverbial babbling brook. I reckoned, though, we were potty, risking it.

When, in convoy, we got to town five miles off at the end of the valley and split, we tooted horns merrily at each other. It was the last communication we would have.

Three hours later, in the newly clustered dark, you're heading back to the farm on the fell. You're excited. Becca's called to confirm she'll definitely be coming tomorrow. Your niece, whom in the slang of the day you 'love to bits', is a sassy young lass quietly trying to mediate between you and her mother. It's an uphill struggle. I've just fancied knocking together the heads of the querulous siblings, but as a counsellor and meditation wallah I'm not allowed to say that.

Meanwhile you have a nice quiet evening ahead, alone, in the old stone kitchen and by the living room fire with Sara and the cats. You like being on your own a lot more these days. You're changing so much. The last photograph of the two of us together, taken the final day of our Greek expedition just over a month before, you look, not sixty-one, but forty. Younger, even. There's a wonderful light in your eye. All over, you're *shining*. We're clinking our glasses of wine, toasting time ahead.

In my diary, 11 October, a week after getting back from the islands and exactly one month before you're dead, I have written: 'I love her very much.'

You're weaving down the rain-lashed valley. Sara, with you, relishes going wherever you take her. She's Jackie's animal but you'd spent years together and were inseparable. She's lying happily on the back seat, ready for her supper, never once barking or making a fuss; gentle, compliant, once-upon-a-time beaten beast that she is – rescued black cross between a collie whippet and a cower.

You come to the bridge that swings right, over the top of the river, and you peel left, past the sign warning you the lane ahead is 'liable to flooding'. You slip down the narrow slope. A bit too fast, could be, shooting downhill? Your driving was often chirpy. Hm? Whatever; I suspect that, in your headlights, and the rain, you mistake the sliding black waters ahead for puddles, or maybe even the still black tarmac of the road.

Splash!

In you go. *'Hello? What the . . . '* – the car's afloat, turns, and you glide away helplessly, surreally, slow-motion, like a novel kind of boat.

The man who sees all this, valley tyre-fitter Tony Middleton, frantically phones '999' on his mobile. He'd been driving behind you down through the vale and stopped by the bridge to make a routine call to his wife. He'd watched you go down Flood Lane then 'hung about a couple of moments' as he wondered if your car would be 'alright', the river 'being a bit up', as he described events to me later. He got out of his vehicle and saw yours returning towards him; he couldn't recall whether you had your reversing light on or were being shoved backwards by floodwater. 'Suddenly,' he'd said, 'the car did a U-turn, and then I realised the driver was in trouble.'

So there you were, illuminated by the interior light, hands on the wheel, 'driving' down the middle of the angry river towards him. Middleton said by his reckoning you didn't look either 'frozen' or 'terrified'. He said, 'She didn't look any different from what she'd be, probably, if you'd met her on the road. Perfectly normal. I was struck by the fact she looked so calm. No panic at all.'

On top of the bridge by then, he could only watch uselessly as your car, passing underneath, headlights blazing, was finally swallowed up down the bends, in the darkness, beyond.

Middleton got hold of his brother on the blower and the two of them went after you on a quad bike. Eventually they found your car, having done another about-turn and now facing upriver again, snagged on a bank of gravel threequarters-of-a-mile down-stream. The Ford wasn't submerged, wholly. The driver's window was down. When you'd passed Tony Middleton by the bridge, you'd had your window up. It seemed clear you'd escaped through the opening.

But of Ruth France, at that point, there was no sign. The head-lights, underwater, continued to illumine but watery wasteland.

Middleton believes you'd realised the lane was 'a bit' flooded but reckoned you'd be able to get through alright, the water perhaps only shallow to begin with. But then, at the precise spot where the river curves across the fields and first touches the lane, he suspects you'd been hit with an unexpected surge, a wall of water gathered from the fells and becks at the head of the valley that had come tumbling down. 'Sheer bad luck and human error' his estimation of what happened.

Once you were in the river and split from the car, you were doomed. The water was travelling at the speed of a cantering horse, and dragging rocks and timbers with it. 'Even an Olympic swimmer couldn't have made it,' said Lee Hill of the police.

The middle of the following day, back in the city – knowing *nothing* of last night's nightmare and the search by police and cave and mountain rescue teams, or the discovery of your body that morning – I get Rob on his mobile from Kenya. I know right away it's not about himself or family that his ghastly cracking voice is speaking. I'd get any bad news about them from you, wouldn't I? No, something awful has happened to *you*.

Rob apologises for being the one who has to break the news, then tells me. The conversation is brief. We'll talk again later.

I sit down, and roar, rocking and struggling for air as though I am drowning, myself.

If only I hadn't come home yesterday afternoon and had stayed an extra night instead, gone into town with you and pottered around while you did your massage, I'd have made damn sure you'd not have gone down that silly sodding lane on the way back to the farm and you'd be alive and kicking, still. Really, I could have prevented all this.

It's all my fault.

ON THE ARCH aptly named Devil's Bridge in the next town, a while later, I stand and contemplate the waters far below and want to go over the parapet, quietly, and join you. I wonder idly what on earth it would be *like*, plummeting through the freezing waters as you did – could one do it contemplatively? Death of this kind, at peace? The police tell me people who've nearly drowned but survived say the end-experience doesn't seem to be terrible. After the initial panic it's a painless 'drifting away'.

The undertaker had said that, the water being as cold as it was, 'it wouldn't have been long' anyhow. A few moments only. Initially you'd have been pulled down and down then, dead, you'd have bobbed up and been taken away like flotsam, to end your days as you did, stripped of everything but your underthings, on that lone and stony shore.

I turn away from the drop and go and drink too much instead (as I do a lot in the long black days that circle now, like vultures).

Days, weeks, pass. It's all over. Kaput. You're a little cylinder of ash, your modest flat's been cleared, and the elegant obituaries are firelighter or fish and chip wraps. The shilling life as I saw it: you were born in rural Sussex, one of four children. Your mum and dad ran a shop. You left grammar school at sixteen and started work as a nanny, then forty-five years later ended your career as one, to your granddaughter Anya shortly before she went off to Africa. In between you were the county's longest serving social worker, renowned for your compassion for abused and damaged children; for anyone, indeed, who cried for help. You fought brave battles in the courts. You'd become quite famous. Married, you had the boys, enjoyed lots of friends, saw your marriage break up, met me and died (no connection I hope). A good enough summary?

The two-bob life, though, might have gone on to record something altogether different, times of almost unbearable darkness; depression that had put you in a psychiatric ward, crippling debt (you still owe me five grand, France), wars with not only your sister but your surviving brother too, problems with menfriends which had left one or two of us reeling, and drink that had threatened your very existence. In short there'd been much in your life that was a mess. No, you were perfectly normal; you weren't a saint.

The last year however had been something out of the ordinary, would you agree? You were a new woman. And the final weeks before your death were, I believe, 'the time of your life'. Its crowning glory.

IT WAS FITTING, I think, that our last adventure together, in this life at least, was in an out-of-the-way corner of the planet the guidebook itself was bold enough to describe as 'paradise regained'. Ever since I was a teenager I'd longed to float around lesser known, 'secret' Greek islands. That literary Hellenic celebrant Lawrence

Durrell had drawn me to the light of maritime Greece like a drunken moth. You'll recall, in the years of my own psychotherapy, executed as dramatherapy, I'd 'played' Odysseus who'd spent ten years wandering back from Troy to Ithaca across Homer's 'wine-dark sea', in my case coming home to Penelope who represented my anima, the feminine in me, my 'soul' as I saw her. And you and I had once gone to Ithaca itself of course to celebrate that unfolding and the light that, in new-found freedoms, was also opening up in you. But in nearly fifty years I'd never got round to it, gone to the isles, bags of time to spare, merely to *wander*. Free. We did so together, finally; no plans, sightseeing, pack-drill. Just that time to 'be'.

The best of times, wasn't it? I had never in my life been more at rest; golden days and silver nights at the back of beyond with the summer people gone and you beside me, joy and laughter and a quiet, a stillness, maybe a song from a breeze in the tamarisks at the back of empty beaches . . . blessings we gorged on day after day, didn't we, in a feast of senses and spirit. And we loved that one particular island in the chain – let's call her, Levitka? – more than them all. Tiny, rocky, home to a couple of hundred souls only, and the main village, the *hora*, perched on the windblown spine overlooking miles of ocean of a palette of many differing blues and further islands hanging in the heavy morning or evening mists like dreams – the place was stunning. 'Our' beach never had more than four or five other folk on it, and often none, and the only sounds beyond the murmuring tamarisks and the slosh of the sea might be the bells of the foraging goats.

Remember a typical evening? Ouzo and nuts outside at the traditional *kafeneio* on the cobbled high street, served by the bent old lady at the little round tables under the bright pink bougainvillaea climbing the whitewash. Just you and I and one or two locals. A cheerful chap on a donkey clip-clopping by. Then somewhere to eat, usually ending up at the open-air watering hole in the square where the raven-haired looker who ran the place used to entertain the whole village with her loud machine-gun repartee and scoldings of the menfolk blanching meekly before her gorgeous struts. And how might we end our evening? With a piece of walnut pie and a thick hot chocolate perhaps. Then, invariably, it was a book at bedtime. We knew how to *live*, did we not? Ha!

Sometimes I'd go away on my own and sit in a deserted cove or out on a headland and, to the wide open spaces before me, offer thanks for my life. I felt I'd had an interesting one – my myriad failings aside, a *good* one? And on Levitka I realised I had never stopped loving you for one moment despite the many sadnesses and fractures of our days together, and I began to wonder, quietly, 'So what now, Ruth?'

The question hovered on our return and was loud and insistent as we came to those last four days of your life we shared at the farm in the Dales. A glorious sixteenth-century restored and romantic eyrie it was, down there in the lower sylvan reaches of the vale with the wild moors and hills around. We'd curl up in the evenings by the blaze in the old range and in silence (the speech of contented hearts) we'd read, nibble sweetmeats, slurp wine, stroke the cats Indy and Minou and, I think, know in some deep sense we'd come to the end of a road. A new one beckoned, no?

I wondered what you might say were I to enquire about moving our relationship on. Yes, after the rather eventful eighteen years we'd known each other (lord, what took me so long?) – 'Will you marry me?', at last.

I WROTE endless love letters to you, didn't I, all through our time together. This to be the last, now. I feel as though I'm calling after you, Ruth, as you're taken by the dark, your tail-lights slipping farther and farther away downriver until there is nothing left of you any longer, except that which remains in my heart. Shakespeare said the best way to make love last for eternity is to write it down so that it outlasts mere human beings. I want ours, you, to be remembered, so much.

Our quest – that *love*, I think, *worthy of its name*? – we were only getting there, of course. We'd not got to the top of Everest had we? Heavens, our flaws and delusions were shockers sometimes. Yet, we were intrepid triers? And I think we had a map. It was the hungry heart pointing across the trackless void *beyond* ideology, religion, philosophy or anything else invented by humankind, to that 'lonely desert place where love is now possible,' as one of my favourite writers expressed it, 'because it finally is wholly free, released of every frantic need to exploit and possess.' (Unless 'love' as I'm embracing it might be something we humans 'invented' as well. I'd prefer though to go with Dante's 'love that moves the sun and the other stars', and such as caterpillars and bats and daisies too. That's to say the mystery of 'love'; the force that drives creation.)

Meanwhile crossing that empty quarter, no 'God' or agency to sustain us any longer, only gathering to oneself the sure knowledge there is at least a better way of living and loving than that soiled by convention's shams and ego's hungers, an awareness watered by a lifetime's tears of pain and loss, the oft-quoted 'long dark night of the soul' (by 'soul', here, I am meaning all that which makes me uniquely, aspiringly, human), I can say on that desolate, trackless night of 11 November I would easily, gladly, have lain down my life for you; would have given you yours, Ruth, if I might drown instead.

IT ALL BEGAN, as it ended, one withering winter's night – at the very spot you'll recall where they filmed that romantic tearjerker, *Brief Encounter*. It was the close of the adult college meditation class's Christmas 'do' at the hotel opposite the station. You'd made somewhat swift excuses and scarpered; you were upset about it being Christmas. I knew you'd been under strain at home, with the end of your marriage and now parenting two growing boys alone. I was concerned about the 'crumpled' exit and came after you, calling your name through the damp septic smudge that's winter night-time in the towns of England. And outside the station, you weeping, I reached out and hugged you. I remember wiping away your tears with my finger. You said you had to dash. 'The boys.' I said I'd phone you.

I was in a relationship at this time, albeit in travail as it was, with the artist Tiana. Now, though, you and I started to meet up, innocently enough, to compare notes on the contemporary horrors of male-female relationships, and drown the pains sometimes in a noggin or two. Some used to raise their eyebrows a fraction at my teaching mental clarity at the same time as I enjoyed a drink. Crazy Wisdom the ancient tantric sages used to call it. Hypocrisy, sniffed one or two of my critics. I believed, however, in trying to balance all things; be man in the street and spiritual traveller, both.

You then invited me one day to come and have tea at your home. I was enchanted. The house was a high, old stone presence up on a bank in the picturesque village beside the estuary wherein the sun sometimes set in flames and across which the little trains chuntered; herons silhouetted in the sparkling waters, distant hills and clouds a-jumble. Around the estuary, often, was a pearly radiance altogether more cheerful than the usual woebegone skies of the North. In time I used to come into the shop on the waterside where you were working a few hours a week, just to watch, be with you a while. You'd given up your social work career for the moment so you could devote more time to the boys. There behind the counter you were so gentle with and attentive to everyone. You had a velvet touch, just the way you were. Other bits of your week you doled out the tea and wiped bottoms as an assistant in a care home. And what became clearer to me the more I got to know you was that you were a woman, in all walks of her life, who *cared*.

You were unassumingly attractive, with dark tousle-haired, brown-eyed looks that reminded me of something distant. Lost. You walked with feet very slightly outsplayed as though, I used to joke, you had a helluva lot of sex. (By your own admission, even in the postmarital upset you didn't do badly in that department, did you? Played the field, rather.) You had some Romany ancestry and were proud of the fact. No, you were not an English rose; you were something more . . . exotic.

I was going through a difficult time myself, wasn't I? Extended midlife crisis. The split between what I taught and wrote and who I was – it was a bit too wide sometimes. The problem was loss. There'd been too much of it in my life, right from the start; born a sickly child, shoved in an incubator, cut off from my mum. Ouch. The pattern was set right there. Today, the spiritual teacher who hailed love as life's highest achievement was at the same time the wounded writer who narrowed his eyes at it a bit (the 'selfish gene'; 'all altruism is at bottom self-interest', etcetera). I confused people, not least myself. And the conflicting dynamic was repeating itself all over again, as these things do, with Tiana. In our case, artist with author, it was as if two suicide bombers had wired themselves up to each other. For a while we emitted glorious paroxysms of sparks resulting in some admirable paintings and prose. Then we blew up. You sat with me throughout, quiet handmaiden to my sorrow. We began *our* story as platonically as we ended it, didn't we?

Remember this though for a history, Ruth? Tiana had finally gone off with one of my closest friends, Roger. Going back a few years before, my second common-law wife, Jenny, had disappeared to New Zealand with one of her lecturers. The first cohabitee, Anne, had secreted a prospective parliamentary candidate into our home while I was away, valiantly toiling over a new book in a remote caravan in the country. My real wife, Wendy, vamoosed with her gynaecologist. My first ever fiancée, Rosemary, cheated on me throughout. My first lover, Wendy Smith of Bournemouth, sent me a 'Dear John' letter while I was off working, aged twenty, in Turkey. My mother, it seemed to me, had gone AWOL not only at the beginning but also after my father had returned from World War Two and, so it felt to me, stolen her away from me. No one ever *stayed*, did they?

I mean, looking at that list, you'd think I was the Elephant Man or a mass murderer wouldn't you? What the hell was wrong with me? I used to mutter. What was *going on*?

I didn't believe any of it but, over twenty years before, a therapist in London had told me that in this life I was 'repairing' much bad behaviour from previous ones, getting my share of karmic come-uppance on the way. Once upon a time for example I'd been a pimp at Versailles. I used to procure women for the king. *Baloney*, thought I, screwing my nose up. Next he'll be telling me I've a 'guide' who's a Red Indian chief or there's the bloody ghost of Nebuchadnezzar in the room trying to tell me something. 'Pass', on this kind of guff, if I may.

Yet not so long ago my ears had pricked up. Another 'sensitive', unbeknown to the man just mentioned and hundreds of miles away, was speaking to me about my patterns in love and sex. Apparently I was dealing with a lot of difficult material. You see there was a time, she said, when I'd lived as a pimp in the French court and generally been 'a naughty boy'. I was rendered open-mouthed, somewhat.

Whatever. It was clear I wasn't conventional marriage material, was I? 'A difficult, moody specimen' maybe? Too challenging of everyone and everything? Simply another ruddy *writer* – 'impossible bastards' that they are, by definition – perhaps? Or was there a deeper truth? Could it be, Ruth France, that I was waiting for *you*? Did we, together, get love 'right' at last?

What was the purpose of this, my life? I'd felt since adolescence it wasn't just to 'survive and reproduce', surely? I'd come to be clear about that. What I wanted instead was to find out what it's all about; what I was capable of; what it might be to be human at the highest level. In the process, though, I was hitting some terrible 'lows', wasn't I?

ALTHOUGH AUTHOR of that book with the grandiosely unlikely title *How To Be Happy* I was, post-Tiana, hit with the blues. I was forced to go on antidepressants and, derailed by the wretched things, had no option but to crawl away to bed. Increasingly my 'best friend', you put me up in the spare room with the boys' football boots and discarded videos, fed me steaming soups and delivered the odd spotted dick pudding. Life had its compensations.

Revived a bit, I used to stagger back into college down in the city to facilitate the classes in meditation and The Meaning of Life, whatever that was. Truly, I was all over the place. Some of my teaching was weirdly inspired, though; in one class, attempting to foster compassion and non-judgmentalism among the students, I 'failed to turn up'. Actually I was hidden away in the cupboard at the back, remember? After about ten minutes' delay the cupboard door springs open and I roll out across the classroom floor on my arse, cold porridge all over my face to simulate vomit, singing some crap song or other, badly. A few in the class were very kind and understanding, others were shocked. Outraged: the teacher was *pissed*, for heavensake! Game plan revealed – I was in truth stone-cold sober – it led to an interesting discussion on our respective capacities for imperturbability and kindness.

Another time, seeking to smash stereotypes and other set ways of seeing, I tootled into college naked but for a flapping dustbin-liner nappy. The face of the college principal as the pair of us bumped into each other in the foyer was a picture. And I used to encourage folk to turn up in fancy masks that revealed parts of themselves not normally exposed to public gaze. 'Crazy Wisdom' again. I think sometimes you wondered whether you might be harbouring a *madman*. Nevertheless there was no end, France, of kindness in you.

I didn't want a relationship. I'd had enough of the damn things. Way back, knocked to bits by one of my earlier romantic debacles, I'd limped up to the fastness of a monastery in Scotland and thought about becoming a monk, had I not? The lama there laughed. The Tibetans did a lot of laughing; it was peculiar. I suspect Akong's perception was that I'd last a month as a monk, max, and thereafter revert to type, wine in one hand, woman in the other. He used to shake his head, wondering why we in the West were so fixated on our love lives. 'Why do you want to put all your eggs in one basket?' he asked me once. 'Why narrow your love down like that? Is crazy! Why don't you learn to love the whole wide world – *everybody* – instead?' I said I had a problem handling a relationship with one person, never mind a global population of zillions. Akong underlined that this was *the whole problem* in a nutshell; all my energy went into one person and when that one soul either disappointed, departed or died, I was left with nothing. I was bankrupt.

I'd come to half a realisation of that internal poverty after my wife had done her bunk and I'd ended up in a mental hospital, howling with what was officially termed 'depersonalisation'. What came out of that episode was dawn of a recognition that, in truth, I'd married nurse Wendy to plug a gaping hole in my life. I *needed* her or someone like her to make me feel whole. Psychological Polyfllla. On my own I felt bereft. Lonely. Frightened, even. The medicine for this condition was popularly termed 'being in love'. And as you and I, both, came to understand about that species of 'love', it was nothing of the sort.

Years back I'd begun to appreciate what was going on and had decided to do something about it, hadn't I? I'd taken off into those solitudinous winters in the mountains, learning to live on my own and enjoy it. It wasn't easy, but in time it 'worked'. Eventually my hermit months and years away in the gales and snows of my lonely mountain cottage became something very special to me. They yielded up the best writing of my life so far, and a new stability and sanguinity too. I was even proud of the fact I'd got to the point I could now manage, handsomely, without a 'love prop'.

Yes, I'd started out in the important direction of learning to like, even love, myself sufficiently so as to refrain from charming, manipulating and, at a very deep level, lying about myself to someone so that they'd do the job for me instead. I understood it was impossible to love someone else, at all, if one did not enjoy or feared being oneself. Love, like charity, began at home. I was conscious, however, that this fresh psychological independence didn't answer all my questions. I didn't want to end up a smiling solitary. I still had relational conundrums and societal imperatives calling urgently for answers.

Akong, the lama with the steel gaze and stillness that let you hear the atoms whistling in the air between you, though only two years older than me, was a kind of substitute dad, 'the wise father', and he began the Herculean task of pointing me to 'the answers'. In the beginning, in 1977, I'd gone to him with a simple request: please could he teach me to meditate to help rid me of stress and depression? He did a little more than that. He spent the next thirty years teaching me how to let go and love. I hope the light he kindled might illumine these my last words, Ruth, to you.

Tiana Marie had been the death throes of an old life. It was time to let *it* go completely. I was content for you and I to be friends, with no demands on each other at all. You, I know, felt the same way. We raised our glasses to our simplicity. And I went on busily giving my wider 'love' to my students, readers and friends in general, trying to live according to what finally I'd committed myself to with the Tibetans, the Bodhisattva vow, the essence of which was plain: 'May I become that source of sustenance which maintains all beings as long as all have not attained to peace.'

'All beings', as writ, I had a sizeable difficulty with, still. To wit, let's say, my mad Polish landlord who had threatened to kill me (truly), the hoity-toity woman next door whose dog regularly and happily shat on my lawn, or my father who'd thrown me out of the family home forever because he'd objected to a book I'd had published, uncensored, about my early life; this lot and more I used to have to suck in a lot of air with in order to maintain some semblance of equanimity in my dealings with them.

Indeed when I went to the family home to see my mother, ex-Windmill dancer cut down cruelly by multiple sclerosis, in the little time left her before she died and had to pick her up from the front drive where my father used to dump her in her wheelchair, frost or rain notwithstanding, because there was no way he was letting me into the house now for even a second, there were moments I have to admit when my thoughts were not so much given to compassion as to murder.

You'll remember the steam coming out of my ears.

And I had problems too with a great deal of the discussion about men that had filled books, newspapers and airwaves for a generation and more now. I took serious issue here with so many women. For me, any single-sex appropriation of superiority built upon the dehumanising of others was fascism. Yet take the *Guardian* columnist, one Georgia Campbell, who'd written, 'I like men, particularly when they're done to a crisp with an apple between their teeth . . . all men are liars.' Or Valerie Solanas, would-be slayer of Andy Warhol who opened her infamous Society-for-Cutting-Up-Men (S.C.U.M.) Manifesto by declaring, 'Every man, deep down, knows he's a worthless piece of shit.' 'All men are Nazis,' roared Andrea Dworkin in one book she wrote, sublimely unaware that by the very hateful generalisation of her oratory she became a species of Nazi herself.

Confronted with that kind of unreconstructed animus I was tempted to empathise with that insufferable old dinosaur, the novelist Norman Mailer, who once said, 'If you women are not willing to recognise that life is profoundly complex and that women as well as men bugger the living juices out of it, then we have nothing to talk about.'

Quite.

No you, France, were different. You liked men.

Bit by bit the road from the city to the village refuge of your home and friendship became the entrance for me to another world, one that would change my life completely. It was a very special drive in itself, once one had left the motorway. It took me, I reckoned, through some of the most beautiful landscape in England; a rolling meld of meadows and deciduous woods snagged with limestone crops where deer watched and danced and the great mountains at last rose up at the back like stage props. The road was always quiet. It had a bit of a curl and lilt to it so the car jigged up and down as though it might be feeling merry itself. Leaving the woodland, finally, there was remnant of the castle on the left, then the craggy presence of the Knott lording it over the village gathered at its foot in yet further crescendos of trees.

How I loved that old road, Ruth, and at the end of it the warmth of your kitchen and hug of your welcome. Even today I cannot drive it without feelings of undimmed affection and longing. I would sometimes contrast the simple joy of those journeys with the desolate ferryings of my mother around her dreary redbrick town looking for a warm café with wheelchair access so we might have somewhere we could park and talk a while, away from my father and his wrath.

I PERSEVERED with my treks to the monastery in the Borders. You'll recall my taking you there sometimes. The lama's one-to-one teaching was simple yet ruthless. In order to come by peace/happiness/love/enlightenment (whatever one might care to call the heart's highest prizing) one had to strip away layer after layer of delusion like onion rings in order to stand square with what would be left. No–thing. The Void. Reality. The emptiness at the heart of the atom. Mind and heart, with nothing to hang on to, in deep rest at last. *That*, said the lama, and the ancient texts, would be 'the pearl without price'.

Akong had even taught me how to do healing. In turn, registered and able to work with it in hospitals and surgeries, I was myself teaching healing too. It was a therapeutic skill anybody could learn, with practice. It was no 'big deal'. I wrote a book about it, dedicated (remember?) to – you.

Like all my other books it made me no real money. Forever struggling wasn't I, mixing meagre royalties with a smidgen from my bits and bobs of teaching and a modest top-up, sometimes, of benefits from the state. It had been like this for nearly twenty years now, ever since I'd given up my job as a television reporter, aged thirty, so I could go and look for a better way to live than 'marriage and a mortgage'.

Still looking, wasn't I?

You and I were a right pair, scavenging as we did, loving the freedoms we enjoyed but sometimes struggling to find enough in your case to put food on the table for you and the boys and me in mine to buy that priceless author's requisite: time. But we managed somehow, as one does. What our lack of money meant, though, was that we much prized the bottle of wine we *could* afford and the tea shop crumpets we might splurge on during our travels on the bikes through the lyrical country lanes around.

But it was on one of those expeditions on the ramshackle old two-wheelers, one summer's afternoon of butterflies and drowse, me some distance behind just watching you up ahead wobble/ wander all over the place – you cycled as cavalierly as you drove, France – the day so jewelled and peaceful, that with a start I stared into the fact, unsettling: I was falling in love with you, wasn't I?

Bang went that resolution, then: 'Never again'.

IT'S CHRISTMAS DAY in the morning, as I write. I've cancelled Christmas altogether as I want to spend the time alone with you.

I sit looking out across the silent city from my huge high windows, at peace. The stupendous view across the crenulations of towers and spires and castle walls to the sea never ceases to lift my spirits. It's a soft grey-blue day with sunshine and not a breath of wind. Everyone in the flats around me has gone away, adding to the intensity of the quiet. The clocks tick loudly. I'll be here with you now for days.

Friends have given me Christmas presents of rations to look after myself with in this retreat with you; things like Wensleydale cheese with apricots, traditional ginger biscuits, macadamia nuts and cranberries, toffee cakes, spiced winter berries cordial, miniature mince pies, multicoloured slabs of chocolate and a very special-looking 2005 Viré-Clessé burgundy, white. Hell, I'll end up a pig. But there is nothing I want really. Except you.

We were supposed to be in Kenya together for Christmas,

weren't we? The plan: to be with Rob, Rachel and Anya, and maybe make it over to Zanzibar too. Then, alas, I had to pull out because of the cost. You, however, were going on your own still. Typical of you; you'd already begun putting together a package of clothes, toys and cash for the children, many the offspring of Aids victims, at the orphanage in the Rift Valley, near the school where Rob and Rachel teach. I didn't know anything about your mission, did I? You'd kept it quiet this end as you didn't want to make a palaver of it.

Anyway, a rather large amount of money, £1,700, was raised at your funeral and Rob is going to take the cash personally, no rake-offs for charity bureaucrats or corrupt African officials, to the children and their helpers in the New Year. It was Chris's idea, and both the boys knew right then it was exactly what you would have wanted.

Ruth, I don't know whether you exist in any shape or form any longer. Core of the lama's teaching has been that I should accept nothing in this life until such time as it is proven to me. Sound stuff. Belief is for the fairies. I have no proof of your individual 'soul' in the strict religious sense, or if you continue to exist in any larger realm of 'spirit'. Chris and Rob buried your ashes just before Christmas in the grave of your mother and father at Herstmonceux, East Sussex, and that may indeed be the end of you full stop. On the other hand I have no proof you don't exist any longer, either. One night last week I was dropping to sleep when I awoke with an electric shock to my body and the abrupt conviction you were there in the room, just behind me as I lay on my side in the dark. I dismissed the whole thing as nonsense. Dozing off again, once more the convulsion and la France, laughing, insisting, 'I *am* here, you know!' My response: 'Codswallop'.

Yet there's so much that can't ever be explained away altogether, isn't there? Your good friend Anne Waters was spooked a couple of weeks back, Ruth. She was talking to someone she knew who at that point had heard nothing about you and your death. The woman – 'highly intuitive and finely sensed' as Anne described her – was 'snagged' on something; she wanted to question Anne about it because, she said, Anne was in some way involved. The interrogator asked her whether she'd known anybody who'd drowned recently. The person who had done so, the woman explained, perished after trying to rescue a dog trapped with her in a car in a flood.

Anne had gone very pale.

So are you here, or aren't you? Gizza 'sign'! (Christmas present to end Christmas presents.)

Nothing.

The day is getting increasingly sunny, a bright blue sky being cleansed of the last of the cloud, and bit of me feels cooped up and lonely; I'm losing my 'peace'. I wonder, stuck here 'with you' in my high white tower, whether I am going mad with grief? Is my mourning, week after week now, making me lose the plot?

I watch the fly wandering around the battered leaves of the ivy, industrious in its hunt for nourishment or moisture, the other side of the windowpane, and I am glad for it. The fly's life, my life – we are both of us alive. We're privileged. We can, both, enjoy this brief interlude of winter warmth on our flesh. You, on the other hand, cannot. Holding gratitude and memories to my heart, I am again at rest.

CHRISTMAS SIXTEEN YEARS AGO, and you and I had just become partners. Tiana, she of the long golden hair and the black highwayman's coats, 'one of the finest watercolour painters in Lakeland' according to *The Times*, another lone wanderer around the Milky Way, was gone.

After their two-year celibate friendship, France and Pepper had come together as naturally, it felt to me, as night and day. That

Christmas, 1992, I shared with you and the boys, your 'ex' Jim and your friends Sue and Gordon, sister Tricia and her husband and daughters, in your snug stone house beside the water. In one of my first love letters to you, just beforehand, I'd written: 'In all my fifty years I have never encountered a more lovely soul.' And I added, 'I mean that.' I did, and to this day do.

Having two teenage boys in my life, suddenly, was novel. I liked them a lot. Rob was all goofy sensitivity and Chris bright, crackling intelligence. Both were exceedingly handsome with it. On your own, you conjured a warm and inviting haven for the two of them and it duly got invaded, all the time, by their brightly spirited pals. Sleepovers were carnivals. At two or three o'clock in the morning I could be lying in bed next to you pondering the ever-receding prospect of sleep, but then next day the house could be quiet as a morgue till two or three in the afternoon when the juvenile assembly would rise as one from its sticky covers, braying for breakfast. You were a wonderfully tolerant and patient overseer. I was the inter-loper on the periphery of things, wandering around with its eyes meeting in the middle. Your place was all of it a fair change from the lordly sanctuary of my then Victorian lair in the city. That first, and last, Christmas with you all was one of the happiest times of my life.

I can't remember details of the first time we made love, save for the slumber afterwards. Your room was at the top of the house, an attic, and used to take in a lot of the silvery light of the estuary across the fields. You were curled up asleep, naked, the sheet draped loosely around your bottom half, all of you, slender and curved, lit with the riverine glow. You were at peace. At that point I knew I wanted to be with you for ever.

In ways then unforeseen it has turned out that way, I suspect.

You liked sex. No holds barred there, were there? You said you'd been lucky, you'd lost your virginity – what a ghastly phrase that is; why not something more affirmative like 'won your woman-hood'? – when you were aged only fourteen (begorrah), your lover an older feller who had treated you with much affection and respect and with whom, thirty years later, you were still friends. You felt you owed him a lot: you'd had a smashing start to life in bed.

You had an appetisingly raunchy side to you, France, and spoke of that fond wish of yours, to deck yourself out in the brightest red dress and the highest red heels you could find and flaunt yourself round the village so as to shock it rotten. 'Wake the place up!' as you put it. You liked dressing up for me, erotic wisps and sheens, and at this period one of your greetings cards to me is the drawing of the back of a dark, curly-haired woman gazing into a mirror wearing nothing but stockings, heels and a fringed silk wrap, bottom bared to the viewer, signed 'Your Gipsy'. This was the nickname I'd come to use with you. You liked it a lot. Remember it all?

After consummation of the relationship you wrote to me saying, 'It was a wonderful weekend, John, quite delicious in every way. Thank you for all your love and tenderness. Never before have I felt so nurtured; so cherished. All the little kindnesses mean a great deal to me too. I love you very, very much.'

I was doolally about you, as you could tell by those endless notes your way: 'I want to read you stories and watch you potter, and kiss your hair; throw scented apples at the moon. Be daft. And hold you close from this day forth, even when we're miles apart.' And so on.

In a tone slightly more sober I wrote, 'I spent fifty years looking for you, but now I see that I have loved you through all time and all seasons.'

I was relieved, so glad that, even though I'd just hit my half-century and had that history of relationships reading like a horror story, I hadn't grown bitter and twisted. I acknowledge it had been a close call at times. Scion of the sixties, I was scornful of orthodoxy and its claims. Relationships as Noah's Ark two-by-twos I'd grown suspicious of. I looked around at what went by the name of love and excitedly underlined what I read in Nietzsche: 'Ah, this poverty in partnership! Ah, this filth of soul in partnership! Ah, this miserable ease in partnership!' And marriage? 'An end of many brief follies' followed by 'one long stupidity'. Fromm's *The Art of Loving* had been a one-time bible, and how did he describe love in our time? As something 'abstractified and alienated, an opiate which alleviates the pain of reality, the aloneness and separateness of the individual.' We had become 'consumers', all. Automatons. And automatons 'cannot love; they can exchange their "personality packages" and hope for a fair bargain. In "love" one has found, at last, a haven . . . One forms an alliance of two against the world, and this egoism *à deux* is mistaken for love and intimacy.' And what did Fromm foretell? 'If it is true, as I have tried to show, that love is the only sane and satisfactory answer to the problem of human existence, then any society which excludes, relatively, the development of love, must in the long run perish of its own contradiction with the basic necessities of human nature.'

'We are now all posthuman,' someone else has just written (here in 2009, in frightening mien), 'a condition in which your "meat-body" – augmented by technology (iPhone, iPod) and drugs – becomes a denatured "e-body".'

And d'you know, in all my life I'd only ever known one couple I'd describe as happy, deeply in love, and whose partnership I viewed with a little touch of envy. *One.*

Yet I'd not 'given up' had I? Despite all the doom-mongering I held a candle to 'love', still. And very much *alive* I remained, didn't I – trying to put into practice, person by person, year by year, all that the lama in the hills had taught me about the essentially indivisible nature of love. You couldn't 'love' some people and not others. That was all to do with ego's attractions and aversions, casting us into the relentless pursuit of one to the exclusion of the other. Doomed us to unending division inside, its pain and ruin, like being bound, the life long, to a wheel of fire.

I had endeavoured to 'love' the fly outside my window just now with the same awareness and compassion as I did you. That was the theory; love as the essence of all that one did, all that one was. As the Dalai Lama himself had once paraphrased in a talk I'd heard him give in London, 'My only religion is kindness.'

In my case I'd had to struggle to live like that; to overcome the cynicism and snap which at one point in my life had I think threatened to turn me into something quite unpleasant; a time I rounded on the world with my wounds. It had made me a sharp commentator on the human condition but a poor physician to it. And it was my anger that cast the first seeds of doubt into your mind about me. Our future.

BUT NOW IT'S CHRISTMAS, and you and I are flying. 'Your honesty and directness are very special,' you wrote to me, 'and I value them greatly. Thank you for all you have brought to my life; the glow I now carry within, a renewed sense of aliveness, and above all an appreciation of a new and very wonderful love.'

In turn I watched the flocks of souls party to your busy existence and wrote: 'I see, from the people who surround you, how much you are cherished in this life.' And added, 'Bless you for leading me to understand what it is to love.'

It's getting dark now. I've enjoyed this Christmas Day with you. My 'Christmas dinner': an apple, a slice of Cheddar and two oatcakes. Enough is enough. We were both of us, weren't we, getting to the point in our lives, lately, where we were wanting to chuck everything, live simply, do nothing that caused harm and be ourselves (last of the bullshit gone). Not for us any longer the magic of Christmas once a year; we were bent on making what time was left us, magical, the long year through.

To that end I've just cracked open a tiny one-man bottle of Casillero del Diablo to toast both you and the goal, which I must now pursue on my own. God (or whatever) bless you wherever you are, if-you-are. Our task at the end, in a sentence, was clear: to learn what it is to love without condition or restraint. Help me to continue to get there. Please?

Happy Christmas.

IT'S WEIRD. My Christmas night reading, and it's all about a woman who drowned in a flood. Isabelle Eberhardt was a Russian writer, adventurer and mystic who became a sort of 'Lawrence of the Sahara'. As in Lawrence's case, she was a legend in her lifetime. She dressed as a man under the name of Si Mahmoud and was much entwined in the French and Algerian struggles at the end of the eighteenth and start of the nineteenth centuries, both as an interpreter and journalist and, some said, 'spy'. A hashish addict, ferocious drinker, member of an Islamic sect called the Kadryas, confident speaker of Arab dialects and confidante of top brass, yet also a self-abasing whore for Foreign Legionnaires, she enjoyed the confidence of the colonialist cause and was entrusted with several delicate missions among Arab leaders. 'No one knows Africa as she does,' one general said. Not yet thirty but worn out, ravaged by drink and probably syphilis, Isabelle met her end in a little shack in a town called Ain Sefra on the edge of the desert.

This, her home now, stood beside a dried-up stream in a ravine. It was the poor part of town with the brothels and mud huts. A thunderous storm in the mountains sent a 'roaring torrent' of water down the dusty riverbed, carrying away houses, cattle, trees and people. Isabelle was last seen on the rickety balcony of her hovel, 'very still' it was noted, 'watching the tide of disaster as it swept around'. Parallels perhaps with the 'calm' of France as she sat at the wheel of her flood-stricken car?

A close friend of Isabelle's believed *she* had made no effort to escape, but in a 'passive exaltation' had allowed death to overtake her. Her body was found two days later, pinned under a broken beam. She was buried in the Moslem cemetery of Ain Sefra beneath a simple marble stone, her name Si Mahmoud in Arabic, the rest, the epitaph, in French. She lay a little apart from the others, facing the desert she loved. I am minded, one day, to try to visit her grave if it remains.

The book in which I'm reading all this bears a title resonating, I think, with the melody of our own story: *The Wilder Shores of Love*, by Lesley Blanch.

I am now constantly drowning, myself. In my tears. Two days before this Christmas break and on the television there are pictures of people in Canada being rescued from a torrent scattering cars like Dinky toys. A mother and daughter trapped in the flood are being winched into a helicopter. Others are being gently pulled from their cars by police. Everyone is saved.

'Why can't *you* have been rescued, for Christsake!' I cry out to the TV set as I crash into sobs, hurling cushions across the room and banging my feet on the floor.

That Christmas long ago I felt I'd been 'rescued' – from, perhaps, an unpropitious fate. Till then I'd wandered the world over looking for a place to be happy, looking for love, hadn't I? I'd lived, making money, as a US air force secretary in a dark little Turkish town where I took to prostitutes to fill my emptiness; on an isolated Spanish beach hoping, hopelessly, to write The Great English Novel and meet the dark lady of my dreams; in a little cabin among the hummingbirds overlooking San Francisco, experimenting with those gladless episodes, orgies; in the Australian bush with an angel who dragged me halfway round the globe and back before popping like a soap bubble; and in just about every corner of England and Wales, falling in and out of love all the while, as I did, like a junkie. And then, as in a sense of coming home, I'd found you. I remember walking with you in the hills one day early on in our acquaintance, through the wind and rain, saying to myself, 'This woman, I know, is going to play a very important part in my life.' Wasn't wrong, was I?

BOXING DAY NOW, and on Boxing Day 'then' it was up to the pub by the water, all of us, and a party in the village. It was known now; I was your partner. Official. I 'belonged'. I was part of the community in this idyllic little place of the glorious marine sunsets and trundling trains. Suddenly I seemed to have the best of all worlds; my base and part-time teaching job in the city, the joy and journey of my writing, a second home here in Blighty, and, beside me, you the gorgeous gipsy with the heart of gold. Felt that Father Christmas had come, that year.

I put my feet up by your fire. I wrote poetry to you.

> So lean forward in the woodglow's end
> Trusting I won't break or bend,
> Let me glance off you with firefly touches,
> You but be the winding river,
> For the moment let me be the giver
> Till you're touched with light all over –
> Let me be the starlight lets you know,
> 'I love you.'

You but be the winding river – what, in a sense, you were going to become yourself one day, hey?

I knew, yes; I wanted this love to last, more earnestly than I had wished for any other. I would commit myself to you and the boys. I was through with the wandering. At fifty, it was time for me to settle. Be still.

You wrote that I 'touched you deeply' with these words, and you 'felt privileged' to be with me. 'It's good to have you there, John,' adding: 'Bless you for all the encouragement and support you provide.' The 'there' rather than a 'here', slightly distancing in hindsight, perhaps, did not register at all in that Merry, Merry Christmas.

Even got on with your 'ex', did I not? I thought the way you and Jim had remained friends was inspiring. Clearly there was love, each for the other, still. I thought he was a good man; kind, gentle and fun. At your funeral we sat side by side. We held hands, briefly. Sometimes I wondered why you'd not made it together. You said you'd just fallen out of love, as people do. Jim had gone off with the headmistress of the primary school after you, briefly, had dallied with a married copper. You'd been first to be unfaithful and that, hadn't it, had troubled you a lot.

The local weasel who was into everyone's knickers in the village (and there was a lot of extramarital de-knickering going on there, by heck) was at the Boxing Day party and I thought he was a plonker. So much for my 'streams of unbridled love' again, therefore. Anyway, he looked suitably shifty in the crowd. (Guy was the same I noticed even at your funeral.)

But it matters not, for I am Happy. And it is Christmas; time for goodwill to all. I get on, most importantly, with the boys. Robin is even talking of getting me to teach him to meditate – not bad for a teenager. Chris wants me to go with him and watch his team, Bolton Wanderers. I draw them cartoons and I think they find me a little bit potty. That's great; anything, please, other than *boring*. Their rooms are disgusting, but I am not going to get involved. They have a *dad*. I'm the part-time resident *loveur*. But yes, I look forward to being their friend.

You were with me so much that festive season of 1992. Are you here now? There is still no serious 'sign'. Everything is changed. You and the boys all gone. No word from either of them this Christmas. Life, I know, sweeps on.

I'll go and have a walk through town this evening to mark the end of Noel. I'll be alone, and I'll be thinking of you, softly intoning the mantra I've been chanting, specifically to whom or what I am never quite sure, the wide world in general anyway, for as long as I can remember now as I've wandered it in my quest for life illumined: just, '*I love you.*'

OF THE EIGHTEEN YEARS, one month and thirteen days you and I were together, just over a hundred days only, three and a half months, were spent in unalloyed partnership. The rest of the time we were in a complex weave of friendship, fall-out, separation, pining, rage, the mutual extending of succour, and spiritual fellowship. Our declared hitch-up started the day after Tiana announced she had slipped off with Roger the Dodger, on 3 October 1992, and ended on 13 January 1993, shortly after that Christmas-to-end-all-Christmases, when I wrote in my diary: 'Ruth ends our time together?' with me adding, through yet more eyes meeting in the middle, 'Here we go again . . . '

Precisely what happened on that day of January 13 I cannot remember, and did not record. Clearly something very important. Whatever it was doesn't matter. What did was the fact that you weren't clear about our relationship after all. *And all those fine words* . . .

This lack of clarity, your uncertainty and ultimately, in consequence, my own, was to be the hallmark of the next sixteen years we shared all the way to your death. All in all it was an amazing time together, hey? A very *modern* love story, I think.

The question mark in that diary entry around 'us' didn't bear fruit. We continued to see each other. It was a horribly potent punctuation mark, all the same. It hovered over our years thereafter like a noose. There were times, I have no hesitation in relating, when I would gladly have strangled you with it. There were times I believe when you *deserved* to be – I think you came to teach me the patience of Job. What on earth was going on? Tell me.

The day, 14 January 1993, after you'd clearly made some reference to ending our relationship, I write to you, heartbroken: 'I don't wholly understand what is happening. I'm wretchedly saddened, of course. Have wept so much at the seeming tragedy of it; a partnership blessed with so much more than in any I can spy around, yet the sublime love at its heart forced to yield to darkling fear.'

That 'fear', your own, seemed to have something to do with my anger, which manifested sometimes. An expression of frustration, say, around the behaviour of the boys, my parping my car horn perhaps at a duffer on the road, or my wanting you to spend more time with me than you were managing; my yearning. Like you, I said, I couldn't live on tenterhooks all the time, 'fearing your fear'.

'If it is farewell,' I wrote, miserably, 'go well. I shall never forget you. The light in your eyes is with me now and will remain always.'

Then, mundanely, I say I'll have to come by at some point and collect the writing tables and chair I'd taken to your place; 'perhaps' (I still had your keys) 'when you're out sometime.'

I ended: 'May all that is best and beautiful attend you; I don't know how I'm going to face life without you. You mean more to me than anyone I have known. This has been ver–y special, and the prospective loss of all fills me with unutterable grief. I wish, so very much, that you could love me as I am and live just this day, leaving tomorrow to God's grace with that love. Whatever, wherever, go gently my dearest friend.'

Didn't stop there, did it? For six months – are we? / aren't we? –

you led me a merry dance. I did not know whether I was coming or going. The joy of Christmas had evaporated like a joke. Two days before my birthday, in June, you *did it*, ended our 'committed partnership'. Spelt it out. On my birthday itself we go out to lunch as 'good friends', and I'm a wreck throughout.

I went to see Akong in his hideaway and get some healing. End of my tether I am. I have spent half the history of time whingeing to Lama Akong Rinpoche about my lost loves and I know by now, of course, the answer. There is no point moaning. Relationships are as changeable, unreliable, as the weather. I need, still, to find stronger anchors in the storms. Keep my love growing, ever farther, out and out. Stop being stickily attached to anyone or anything. Stay free. *Be* love, not 'in love'.

That night I'm back home and who comes over? No prizes for guessing that one. You are, I note happily in the diary, 'grieving'.

And five weeks after you've pulled the plug on 'commitment', where are we? On the Ionian island of Ithaca. Romantically entwined.

You'd got us a free billet in the 'country cabin' belonging to a friend. This turns out to be a corrugated iron shack heating up like an oven in the sun and home to an army of hyperactive rats. At night we hear them scampering over the metal struts in the roof a few feet above our faces and attacking the food stores beside our beds. Much of the night is spent chasing the blighters with the torch. One doesn't get much sleep. In the end, night two or three, I drag my cot into the open at dawn and plead for repatriation. One bloody rat follows and perches on its hind legs on the end of the springs like it's auditioning for *Tom & Jerry*.

Swimming in the lustrous waters below the heights where some say Odysseus sited his castle, I, attempting to recover from the rats, am stung more than once by jellyfish.

On the way to the 'alleged' Cave of the Nymphs where the old Trojan trooper lodged his Phaeacian treasure before going on to explain himself to his wife after his decade-long 'jolly', our moped up-ends on the rise to the entrance and you and I end up on our backs in the gravel, bruised, machine on top of us both.

You then run out of money (story of your life) and we have to 'SOS' England.

Yet. And yet. We've found ourselves a new home, a tiny flat in a garden of olive trees without rodents, and each morning we collect fresh bread from the baker down the lane and begin days of delight wherein our fogs of the past six months dissolve in the sunshine. Or seem to. We're like newlyweds. There's so much sex we live in a cloud of steam. I stagger round the village in my sarong, bow-legged. Wonderful ads we are for menopausal madness.

Jesting aside, these days *were* special. The photographs show us so relaxed now. I love the one of you with your book on the jetty wearing nothing but your smile and a sunhat, and the other where you're laughing prettily with your ice-cream (after you died they put that one in the paper). There's the reflective Ruth in the dark of the Orthodox church before the tall blazing candles. In bed, almost virginal you look, beneath a crisp white sheet. Looking naughtily to camera, caught out, cardi around your shoulders and a glass in your hand, naked again after we have just made love on the night beach overlooking the lights of Cephalonia across the water. The ones of myself where I no longer seem to have a care in the world.

Nevertheless, they were still the times I, uncertain, am working tirelessly to try to win your certain affections. Another poem I wrote for you, and again the fated image of the water that is feared so much:

> *Midnight: a dark pool across which they*
> *Face the other,*
> *Afraid to enter.*
> *For one, the fear of commitment,*

The other, a terror of loss;
Waters haunted by moony shapes of a father
She could never please enough,
And a mother he would lose to please Father.
How, then, to meet when parted by the past?
Take off your parents' hand-down clothes
And burn in understanding's fire,
Then cool the ash with tears that free you
From and for them, thus yourself,
And, naked, wade into the deep,
To swim at dawn in trust's embrace;
Another way of saying – love.

Ithaca, for you and I, was that 'wading into the deep' of our shared odyssey. Odysseus's long journey back to his kingdom had been mooted as a tale of the psyche seeking its way home through the trials and tribulations of our days. We go out into the world to fight our battles, as Odysseus did at Troy, and come by adventure, fame and fortune along the way, but the time unfolds when we grow weary and feel a deep need to come home to ourselves as we are, without all the *things* we have gained. Odysseus, after all, has no need of his trinkets in the end. Ithaca as mythological quest was celebrated by Cavafy in his poem of that name, in which he said that to arrive there is our 'ultimate goal'. Ithaca, says Cavafy, has given us 'a beautiful voyage'. Without Ithaca we 'would never have taken the road'. The Christian take on the story is a long journey beset by temptations, setbacks and danger; an allegory for man's earthly experience and his preparation for heaven. On my own road as Odysseus in my dramatherapy I had come back to Ithaca after more than four years of struggle in which I had travelled through my past and even slain my father in order that I might be free of him at last and thereby love him more. Home in

Ithaca, I was confronted by the fabled one hundred and eight suitors. These I saw as vestigial aspects of myself needing some dissolving too. I 'slaughtered' a hundred and seven of them in merry bloodbaths but the final suitor eluded me. I was in agony for weeks, trying to find him. Dig him out. 'Sort' him. Then it dawned on me who this last, elusive figure was. It was my ego. And of course that would be around, embodying fear in every cell of my being, till such time as I had let go of all that I clung to and had come, instead, to live lightly, as love. When I'd done that, I wouldn't have to 'slay' the ego; that could be befriended with the rest.

But back in Ithaca, 1993, even amid our strange resurrection and its joy, we are both of us much stalked still by fear. Ego is out there, ever on the 'pull'. In truth you and I at this time have yet to 'come home to Ithaca'. We're hopelessly stranded, leagues distant, in leaking lives.

Two months after we're back in England you write to me: 'I begin to see how mixed up I am about so many issues, but especially the relationship between you and me. I know how you feel about me, how fond you are of the boys and how much you enjoy sharing our lives, but I realise more than ever right now that I have nothing more to offer. You could hang around forever in the hope of having a future here, but I owe you the truth, and that is this: I do love you but I don't want to share my life. We've had many wonderful times together but I cannot envisage a time when I would be ready to commit to anyone again. I know I'm throwing so much away but my need to be alone and free grows greater. I think we should stop seeing each other, for both our sakes.

'Doing this to you again pains me deeply. I'm only too aware of the hurt I've already given you, and appreciate too well the effect of this letter. However, it may somehow provide an opportunity (for you) to deal with your scars over "abandonment" once and for all, and you may enter into your next relationship without that fear. You deserve so very, very much, and someone out there is waiting for you. Your beauty, capacity to love, kindness and sensitivity are rare in a man – you've touched my heart so deeply but still I hold back from opening further.

'I hope one day you will forgive me. It hasn't worked out for us as lovers, but at some later date I pray we may be friends, and that you will thank me for stepping aside. *Believe me* when I tell you something better awaits. You do have people in your life who care – please reach for them to help you through this time.'

Start of the following month I'm tutoring a university summer course titled 'Celebrating the Single Life'. I feel like issuing the eight students with pistols and recommending they blow their brains out. The Single Life, folks, is unmitigated shambles.

I write to say goodbye to the boys. 'Ruth is so very beautiful to me, and I have never loved anyone so much before in my life. And accordingly I have grown to love you, too. Know that part of me will remain with you always.'

Just before the year's out you come over to see me for the day. We have, you tell me, what shall be 'our last' sexual encounter. The End. It is, I note, 'sad, sexy and so very, very loving'. The reason this really *is* the finale, you inform me by letter three weeks into the New Year, is because you are in a new relationship, with someone else.

Driving my old banger round the country lanes as though I've been hit over the head with a shovel, scattering deer and ramblers with not-so-gay abandon, I arrive at your house, that appalling winter's afternoon, to drop your keys through the letterbox. This is it. *Finish*. I don't want to but do it all the same. I decide to knock on your door. I half-knew what to expect, didn't I? It's not opened by you; it's opened by *him*. I get a blast of the lovely warm air emanating from the Aga in your homely kitchen and see he's really got his feet under the table, then. I am so traumatised I cannot to this day recall a single feature about the man. He was civil enough. No, you weren't in. He took the keys (I couldn't even muster the energy to explain who I was, though I knew he knew) and quietly closed the door on my brimming tears. Goodbye, History.

I go home, a long way from the letters your way that used to say things, a-hem, like: 'I would like to retreat to the deep corners of the bed with you tightly skirted, heeled, and open you out like an anemone and come upon you in a tide; make you starshape too, finger to toe, and feast upon every slick and salty cranny of you till you shake with drift, helplessness; touched with gleams. I want to smell you. Lick, and slide.'

Ah those dim and distant days. Yes. The last part of life's road, though, noted some sage or other, has to be walked in single file. I think I'm approaching that stretch, slowly.

I'VE JUST BEEN OVER to see my dad and wish him Happy Christmas, such as it may be for a ninety-one-year-old in a care home far away, on his tod. The place stinks. He gets a sausage thin as a constipate's stool in a dead white roll, and they call it 'supper'. But he's cheerful enough. You always asked after him and were glad to hear his 'latest'. His 'latest' this visit concerns a new female arrival down the corridor who keeps making a pass at him – so he reckons. She's 'bonkers'. She assails him with 'a long dribble coming out of her mouth' and he has to scuttle past her open siren door as fast as he can. That'll keep him fit. What keeps him sane are the notes he pins up on walls railing against the management, or writing things like 'village idiots cared for by halfwits' as his assessment of the place on feedback forms. Dad has a problem making friends. He prefers his own company. Good job, I suppose. After all our wars I have come at last to love the old blighter and lately I've told him so, as you know. He assured me he loves me too. Once upon a time I had visions did I not of breaking into the collapsing wreckage of his house, pinning him against the wall by the throat, and killing him. Really did. He never quite apologised for throwing me out of the family home all those years ago but has now acknowledged, 'I've done some things in my life I shouldn't've. I'm not proud of.'

I love him because, as Larkin wrote, all that's left of us in the end (of any merit, I take him to mean) is love. All that's left of thee and me; this union of ours that is my greatest teacher (Akong architect, France the task) and endures beyond custom's point of exit, 'till death us do part'. You aren't the Ghost of Christmas Past so much as spirit, I hope, of enlightened Christmases to come.

SO YOUR NEW YEAR OPENS with you in the arms of another feller. I know nothing of him save you'd met like you and I had, at night school. The curse of adult education, I grumble / hiss. Oh, he's called David.

David, Ruth, you're like a pair out of the Old Testament. I feel like visiting a dollop of Old Testament wrath, plague and fire on the hypnotic house by the water I sometimes can't help passing ('can't help' be jiggered – truth is I used to do a thirty-six-mile round-trip sometimes just to hide in the hedge across the road and hope I might catch a glimpse of you coming in or out and get sight of the man who's rendered me redundant; to mourn hugely, clutching my pain to my chest like a knife there as, in the dark of the night, I watch your downstairs lights go out then your bedroom light come on, then go out again, to be replaced by a wretched romantic candle, whereupon I visualise in horrible technicolour detail what he is doing to you as you unfold 'starshape, finger to toe' for the bastard.) All this after I have just written on page one of a new diary: 'Solo, sad'.

Though I'd written that farewell letter to them, the boys have told me no matter what's happened between me and their mother, they'd like to go on seeing me. They said they 'cared' for me. Shocked, delighted, I agree then: we'll stay friends. What a touching gift they bestowed on me, yes? So I continue to see them, at my place in town, a football match, or down the snooker hall. Each encounter, precious.

They're very loyal, rightly so, to their mother and hardly breathe a word about what's going on back at Woodlands. What I do learn, though, is that 'David' is ensconced there full-time. At that point I think I must have opened and shut my mouth like an expiring trout. Ruth, you have but a few short weeks ago written to me declaring that you 'need to be alone and free'; 'I don't want to share my life' – remember? 'But I do love you.'

It transpires, oh how it transpires, via the bush telegraph that's life in the sticks, that David Whatshisname (I deliberately never bothered to find out his surname and didn't know what it was for *years*) is not only *living full-time with you*, something I never managed once; he is also pretty much *being kept by you*. Apparently he's homeless, jobless (apart from a gardening stint here and there) and hasn't a penny.

It is, I rage inwardly and a fair bit of the time outwardly too, social worker France at it again. Charity all-consuming. *Sick?*

I would think like that, though, wouldn't I? And I didn't want to hear the business at all about 'David' being something of a meandering 'spiritual teacher', a 'shaman' apparently. Crikey, that was supposed to be my kind of billing with you, wasn't it, France? What are you up to, woman?

I am, not for the first time, lost. Jim, the policeman, me, now this new wallah; in another calling up of your deepest fear, not long back you'd mourned, 'I've *drowned* in relationships.' That was why you 'didn't want any more', couldn't I see? But I'd pleaded with you in another of my letters to let me take your hand 'and lead you gently towards the deeper ends of the pool or river,' not because I desired 'to drown thee' but to encourage you, through having enough confidence in me, to let go of your fears and go with the flow, and *float*. No, I wrote, I didn't want to 'join you behind rusting bars in the name of "partnership".' I was adamant: 'Ruth, intimacy that "drowns" or "suffocates" or "diminishes" can't last. It kills. I've spent my whole adult life struggling not to allow my spirit to be caged, so that it can freely fly.' You and me, I'd sought something 'new and special' for us. Spiritual. Winged. Instead now you've settled for . . . what? Truth was, I did not know. Maybe David's an angel? You've chosen well? Compared to him, I'm a lead balloon?

No, I *am* lost. And I know from all the work in my spiritual life that this is an auspicious moment. When that which I most long for might at last be found. When, truly, I might, yes, 'fly'. I have to say t'rar to you after our lengthening entanglement. In 1994 I'll see you no longer; will give my love to the boys, and the world beyond them. I have to let go.

Cut.

INSPIRED IN MY READING by the psychotherapist Carl Rogers, who believed that through 'being real' and the extending of empathy and unconditional respect, human beings related to one another at their best, thereby bringing about healing between themselves, I decided I'd try to become a counsellor. After the long years working in groups in college and university settings, teaching people to meditate, to look afresh at their lives and reach out to one another with therapeutic touch, I now sought the deeper intimacy of working psychologically one-to-one. It was all of it a cash-in for the deeper intimacy I'd failed to find in my love life (though did have in bucket-loads, I liked to believe, with my friends), and was precisely the kind of intimate engagement in the world beyond my private one the fleeting light-sword smile of the lama would readily lend itself to. 'Tenderness' was my favourite word in the English language, and now was the time to go forth and practice it big-time, heart to heart.

As a consequence of my having written those few books in the field of personal development and taught same I was allowed to skip early sections of counsellor training and go in at the deep end, year three, advanced diploma, at one of the best training bases in the subject in England. Your kicking me into touch when you did, Ruth, was the best thing you ever did for me, and I mean that without the smallest nip at you. You freed me to go out and find that which, I was to come to realise, was what I most wanted to do in all the world. Counselling was to become my life.

The words one soaked up at this time of an immensely demanding apprenticeship, so far removed in kind from any other one might have embarked on, were manna: 'What does it mean for a person to possess the quality of tenderness in all its fullness? In the first place it is the quality which irradiates the total person – it is evident in voice, the eyes, the hands, the thoughts, the feelings, the beliefs, the moral stance, the attitude to things animate and inanimate, seen and unseen. Second, it communicates through its responsive vulnerability that suffering and healing are interwoven. Third, it demonstrates preparedness and an ability to move between the worlds of the physical, the emotional, the cognitive and the mystical without strain. Fourth, it is without shame because it is experienced as the joyful embracing of the desire to love and is therefore a law unto itself. Fifth, it is a quality which transcends the male and female but is nevertheless nourished by the attraction of one for the other in the quest for wholeness.

'It will be evident that so breathtaking a quality is rare. What is more, no one person can hope to embody it more than fleetingly and intermittently, for to be irradiated by it is to achieve a level of humanness which belongs to the future and not to now. It is precisely for that reason, however, that those of us who have chosen to dedicate our lives to counselling and to the education of the person have the awesome responsibility of developing this quality in ourselves and others now. If we can do this in our generation, then we can have hope that there will indeed be a future and that it will be a time in which something qualitatively different can happen between human beings.'

This by a hugely challenging exemplar of the person-centred tradition in counselling in Britain, Brian Thorne, who described therapy at its best as an encounter between two human beings who have 'given themselves and each other permission to risk being fully alive'. He adds, 'At such a moment I have no hesitation in saying that my client and I are caught up in a stream of love.'

Such a different image, suddenly, to that I've been holding for so long now, your being carried off in that 'raging river of murder'.

But what exactly was this 'love'? It must, Thorne said, involve the deepest commitment to understanding. Love devoid of such, he stated, 'although it can bring comfort and solace, can never heal.'

At that time you and I, self-evidently, lacked such understanding, and our love, hit by successive waves of misunderstandings, was doomed. It was true, both of us had known 'comfort' and 'solace' in our sharing, and more, but what had finally consumed it, and us, was (yours and mine together) fear. Australian artist and writer Michael Leunig has posited the idea that in life there are broadly only ever two feelings, two languages, two activities, two motives, two procedures, two frameworks and two results – simply, love and fear.

Love and fear.

Ruth, goodbye. I'm starting my life all over again.

And what happens? A year later a certain lady phones out of the blue on my birthday and offers me the gift of a massage. *It's you, of course*. You've gone and qualified as a masseur while I've been training as a counsellor. I melt into your hands and push the boat out. Will you come back with me to Ithaca? Let's!

You're not sure; you go away and think about it. I ask you again. There's more dithering. But finally you weep and shake your head. *No.* You're sorry.

You're still with 'David'. You're getting fed up having to house and feed him. He's a lazy sod. He talks a load of tosh sometimes. Your relationship with him, you've no idea where it's going, if anywhere. Oh my.

Are you as exhausted as I am? *Ruth*?

Screaming quietly, I head for the hills. Ruth: *goodbye*.

A STRANGER, a woman, comes into my room at the doctors' surgery where I'm starting out on my counselling practice, and after half a dozen sessions is able to report, after much struggle and suffering in our encounter: 'I want you to know I'm very happy. I'm in charge of my life again. I know where I am now. You mightn't think you've done anything, but you have, you've been a great help just being there. You've never judged me, you've not said to me, "Well do this, do that, do the other" – you've made me look at things which a few weeks ago I didn't want to look at. You've never made me feel threatened, and that's why I feel such a good rapport with you.' When, mission accomplished, she says goodbye there are tears in both our eyes.

My first would-be 'suicide' and within my own sorrows and uncertainties, even, I am able to reach out to a stranger in a way I have never quite managed before. I feel composed. Strong. In my notes a tape transcription: 'I just want you to know I'm with you in your pain, and I feel for you. It must be awful to be going through this. I guess I'd like to be able to give you an answer to your troubles. I can't. But I'm with you as a companion in what you're going through; I'd like you to know I'm here for you in whatever way I can be of help. I do feel your loneliness very deeply.'

Indeed. It's my own. There'd been a time in my life when I'd been suicidal. After my engagement to Rosemary had unravelled I had tried to kill myself with a cocktail of aspirin, nembutal and wine. That I'd survived, said the doctors, had been 'a miracle'. The colour of my flesh when I was rushed to hospital was 'black'. Today, though, I have found my calling, and life hereafter will never be the same. Akong quietly snortles, and smiles. I owe him.

I owe *you*.

I CANNOT COUNSEL YOU. I cannot counsel friends, or anyone I know. There's too much history that would get in the way of my being the empty mirror that might reveal the other to themselves as they really are. I do, however, listen. I'm your friend, even now your friend. I cannot hate you or turn you away, or deny you anything that might be mine to offer, because I know, Ruth, I love you still. Yes, we are back in touch – with exclamation marks, and rightly so, in the diary.

We sit beside the sea that winter's day and you tell me about David, and how you find so many things are 'wrong' with him just as they were, of course, with me. But you can't turf him out. He has nowhere to go. Being you, you won't kick a man when he's down. I listen, the wind in the long grasses on the marsh, the ripples of the pools, and it's not a triumphal smile I raise; it's a sad one, warm, and I lean forward and kiss your head, your gipsy's windblown hair.

I'm afraid to ask you this because of what the answer might be, but I need to do so all the same: 'Ruth, why David rather than me?'

You play with a little crumpled sand-pie at your feet. It's the colour of England. The weather's bitterly cold. Sometimes I look out across this great bay of ours and reckon we could be in Siberia. I yearn to be somewhere warm and light.

Far away, with you.

'He's very quiet.'

I bristle a bit; the quiet accusation my way in your words. 'What d'you mean exactly?' I am trying very hard not to sound unquiet; up for a squabble.

'He's easy to live with.' The inference being, I'm not. I say so. You look worried; you hate confrontation. Every time, everywhere, you have to keep the lid on things; be everything to everyone. Yes it does, it makes me feel cribbed. I don't want to be nice. I want to be real. You add, 'Not all the time, no.' Easy to live with.

'What was it about me, then, that made you uneasy?' Do I want to hear all this? I do. The truth shall set you free, and all that. The drive, isn't it, the whole of my life. The water in my eyes at this moment isn't all to do with the wind off the sea. I am now sure I shan't like what I am going to hear.

'You're always fighting; the whole world it seems sometimes. All the time – it can get, I don't know . . . unrestful.'

'Don Quixote tilting at windmills!' I proclaim, proudly, in my defence. 'Yeah, I do fight. For justice, for things that matter. For the little guy. Causes that are, what? – *right*.'

'True,' you said, 'and I admire you for that, John, you know I do, but I've different preoccupations. I've the boys to think of and right now I've to focus my entire life on them.' You shook your head, to try and shake the tangle out of it.

'I got on very well with the boys. Still do. I see quite a lot of them even now as you know.' We're wandering away from the issue, as one does in these stock encounters where justification is on the rampage, scattering insight and understanding like startled rabbits, and wrecking all chance of accord. 'How does David get on with them, then?' I cap my pirouette with the tiniest snarl.

'Alright.'

' "Alright"? What does that mean?' And I see in a flash what the practice manager at the surgery has just meant while appraising my counselling at the end of my placement there; lots of lovely words capped, though, with the message 'You're a very intense person, aren't you?' I'd have preferred the word 'passionate' myself, but still.

'Oh, John,' you sighed. Softly pleaded. 'I don't know . . . '

We sat listening to the wind and the birds for a while. There's not another human being in sight. But I cannot let go, can I? 'We never rowed. I can't recall one time we had a real set-to, you know that? We didn't fight. Yes of course there were times we didn't see eye to eye and I used to get irritated and moan a lot, I hold my hand up to that, but we didn't . . . didn't shout and stuff. Did we?'

'No, but you were *angry* quite a lot of the time.' That was the killer word in our association wasn't it? Anger, which took you all the way back to your childhood when you'd always feared it, no matter whence it came; although any outbreak of ire from your father upset you especially. Anger, all round, that scared you stiff – put you out of touch with your own wrath for ever.

Until such time, that is, that it started to kill you.

At this time it was your trump card against which I had no serious hand in response, other than my love, pitted and imperfect as it was. It wasn't enough.

'And David doesn't get angry?'

'No.'

'He doesn't get angry, you don't get angry – sounds as though you're living together in perfect peace. Why then isn't it working, Ruth? Hm?'

'I don't know why.'

I have my suspicions of course. My time in psychotherapy, the sojourn with the lama, the counselling training and growing clinical experience, the lifetime studying the ways of the heart and our hopeless starvation and mutilation of it in the rubbish world we've come to inhabit; all these things lead me at this moment to say, 'Maybe it's because it isn't real.'

'You may be right.'

That afternoon in the marsh was, I think, genuine enough. When we got up from our perches on the rocks we gave each other a hug that felt so.

'Where do I fit in with things these days then,' I wondered, *fake*-lightly, it has to be said, 'in your life?'

'I'll always see you as my friend. A very dear one.'

I continue to try to be such, too, for the boys. I surprise myself; how much they mean to me, still. I remember the first time I'd gone out with Robin on our own together, when he was just into his teens. We'd kicked a ball around on the wide swathes of the estuary green where once they cut the turf for Wembley. I enjoyed his quiet ways, the humility, the sense of something deep and important working its way through him as he grew into manhood. He never once tried to impress me or anyone else as far as I could see. I think he was constitutionally incapable of boasting. He was drawn to martial arts, magic, the meaning of things and, in keeping with the adjective I've used already to describe him sometimes, 'goofy', doing nothing but 'goofing around'. He was always exceedingly laid back and I never saw him get angry or upset about anything, although he took any defeat of his football team, Leeds United, rather silently. In a bedroom that was replica of a warzone, he could sleep for England. Chris, the elder, was, by contrast, more keyed up, excitable, full of brilliant ideas, whether to save the world or to make a million, and the potential for battle. At St Andrews university, already a fervent member of the Labour Party, he got to be vice-president of the students' union and there was talk, wasn't there, of his setting his sights, maybe, on going into politics. I loved being with them both and don't recall ever having a fall-out with either.

Of course they ragged me rotten, old fart that I was. When they were of age, we drank a fair bit together didn't we? On the football front I used to take flak for supporting Southampton, who were generally useless. It was fun 'parenting'. And sometimes you joined us as well, especially just before Christmas when the four of us would go out for dinner together like any normal family only, eventually, for you three to peel off to catch the last train back to David and the life you all had with him, and I would walk away to Christmas with others, or on my own.

Interludes that made the separation between you and me all the more painful.

David, now, was going to train to become a counsellor too. His life seemed to be following mine like a shadow. It was macabre. I asked the boys, of course, how they got on with him.

'Alright.'

Did I hold out hope even now that one day you and I might get back together? Yes I did. How come? I don't know. It was a feeling.

There was no more sex, nor ever a hint of it. I still found you attractive but think I'd grown a bit afraid of your mood swings. I was determined I wasn't going to be hurt by you again. Besides, your cunny was home now for another (expelled I was from paradise).

Once we were discussing our 'situation' and you reckoned the best description of the pair of us might be 'brother and sister'. It made some sense. You'd had a very difficult time not only with sister Tricia but also your surviving brother Keith, and I with my sole sister Linda. All these sets of relatings were battlegrounds even today. (So much, alas, for our meditations, spiritual aspirations and whatnot then. Not good, was it?) So yes, I was your idealised brother and you my perfect sister.

Sometimes, though, when I caught sight of you inadvertently turning to fill your skirt with your ample bottom and noted the line of your ever shapely legs, I'd sigh a tad at the 'arrangement'. I couldn't forget the times you used to come to me at night with a flower in your hair; that famously wicked look in your eye. You did, you made a succulent harlot. 'My spiritual sister' – oh dear, sounded the stuff did it not of wimples or the dreary Methodism both of us had grown up with as children. What about that fantasy of yours, then, where you'd be dolled up like Cleopatra at a posh party and have a room to the side wherein at intervals throughout the night every man in the house would quietly come to you, one by one? And my not dissimilar, reverse, confection? No, we buttoned our underwear and behaved.

You were now, you reported, having to lend David money, which was a turn-up for the books. These days he did next to nothing but 'hover' around the house and you couldn't get him out from under your feet. You, who'd craved 'time and space'. He was driving you *mad*.

Nothing to do with me. Once more with feeling, I got on with the rest of my life, unsure as ever, though, as to its express direction. Hadn't I, I'd rejected 'golden opportunities' time and again. You knew I'd been a prize-winning journalist working with what were to become some of the best-known names in British television: Michael Palin, John Humphrys, Michael Buerk, Martyn Lewis and others. Remember my sometimes pensive looking back at being offered the prospect of posts as BBC correspondent in San Francisco, or Rome, and assistant editor of the *Reader's Digest* in Sydney, and my deciding no to the lot. *The Times* in London saying, 'Come aboard, travel where and write what you want.' I still said, 'Sorry'. I was crazy, yes. I simply followed hunches which said, 'You're going to do something else, more useful.' I was always convinced this would be the case one day.

I think that's what you and I shared so much, that wish to be 'useful'. We didn't pine for fame, fortune and fantasy. There was, more, a quiet wish for a life that might *mean something*.

I still find it hard to define those words. The two of us often laboured to make sense of them, didn't we? We were talking about them all the way to your death. Neither of us could find a resting place in the world of shopping and sex. Nor one either in religion and pie-in-the-sky. Workplaces were invariably hell-holes and working at home hellishly lonely. Cities were brutal and villages boring. Families drained you and single living could so easily have one slamming the door against the whole caboodle. Money made one smug; lack of it, miserable. Forever, the warring antinomies. Those divisions inside in need of healing.

For nearly twenty years now, however, I had come by some meaning that made sense. It was in the love I'd borne you. It was an expression, I believed, of that which was most authentic in me. You had been the eye of my storm.

But at the end of the day, sadly, I had to let you go also. Utterly. There *was* nothing left to hang on to at all.

I HAVE TO ACKNOWLEDGE that, as I left the chapel of rest that morning after you'd gone, thanked the undertaker and shook his hand, and set off down the hill to home, there was some strange sense of relief amid the tumble of my feelings. If I couldn't have you, what else was worth the 'having' any longer? My health perhaps. But one day that was likely to vanish too – and what then? Would I at that point be able to dwell peacefully in the storm?

I had some hope. Genetic, maybe. My father had no complicated inner life like I had, he was a no-nonsense sergeant, an original, Irish Guards, 'Sergeant Pepper' who reckoned the good he'd done in his nine decades on the planet marginally outweighed the bad and, in consequence, when his time came he'd be escorted up to Heaven by angels and there be reunited with my mother. In the meantime, tied to a piss-bag, sometimes soiling himself, forever getting struck down by pneumonia but surviving, downing Chinese takeaways to offset the in-house diet, crumpled up in front of the telly till all hours and feeding his unending prejudices with the *Daily Mail*, and waging endless war with the care home establishment, he 'got on with it' with a stoicism and gruff humour I'd come to admire immensely. He had next to nothing left in his life but he wasn't afraid of dying. He said so. Plain. And often he reported, 'I'm perfectly happy, thank you.' I hoped I might have inherited some of his legacy of the less cantankerous kind.

I was drifting. You and I, both, were feeling in need of new lives, weren't we, even though you had by now, yourself, gone back to your old one as a social worker. So what do we do? We go off together to somewhere different this time.

Bosnia.

FIRST OFF I'D VOLUNTEERED to do some summer healing work in Sarajevo on my own. The Bosnian war had ended only a couple of years before and the capital city in which nearly eleven thousand people had died and four, five times that number had been wounded in the longest siege in modern warfare – almost four years – was a wreck run largely by the Mafia. The poverty was heart-rending. Menace hung like a gas.

The charity I hitched to offered therapies to victims of the war, mostly civilians cut up by mortars or shot by snipers. Children who'd starved underground in shelters and got little rest, exercise or sun had often been turned into hunchbacks. Unemployment was seventy per cent. 'Welcome to Hell' or 'Paradise Lost' the ubiquitous graffiti.

Civil engineering director Rašidagić Nihad told me that, if Bosnia did fall back into bloodshed, 'that'll be it – it will be finished, and will burn end to end.'

I worked in a cramped clinic downtown alongside Muslim medics and masseurs or, interpreters in tow, out among the vast estates of Soviet-style towers that had often been reduced to a rubbled echo of Stalingrad but among which people lived still, like rats, many too sick or wounded to get to the clinic or any other medical help. My offering: the therapeutic touch I'd taught at college years before. The Bosniacs were less cynical about healing than was the case back home; they called it 'bioenergia', rooted as it was in Bosnian folk-healing traditions. The rationale behind it was as simple there as it was anywhere: if the practitioner through her stillness and focus could take the client to a place of deep rest (into a light trance, in effect), then the client's natural resources could be galvanised, and do their work of repair. Trauma, stress and fear interfered profoundly with this innate healing process. The therapist's task was to put the wounded person back in touch with just that. It wasn't New Age nonsense; it was a history of natural medicine going back to the beginning of civilisation, *energy follows thought* its essence.

At home, you were already marrying your massage to healing. After my solo stint in the field I felt you would have a lot to offer. Would you join me the following year?

I think Sarajevo was the point in our lives when we came together and at the same time split apart the most. We did a lot of our work, just the two of us in tandem, at that lovely big house, remember, in the jumbled old quarter the charity had converted into a sanctuary for victims of the war. But, as before, there was the need to get out into the city to help others afflicted. I recall with awe and admiration the work you did with women from the rape camps, haunted creatures, broken glass, and the smiles and laughter I was privileged to witness at the close of your all-too-brief sessions with them. I cooed and joshed with the men who'd lost legs and arms or bits of them but were tickled pink with your ministrations with their phantom limbs; weird yet wonderful it was to stand beside you as you massaged apparent thin air while patients let you know very clearly – 'Ooh! Agh! Up a fraction. No, down a bit. Oh God yes: just there!' – how much the energetic matrix of the lost flesh responded to your touch. The children thrilled to you, as children invariably did, the little Romany boys and girls dancing round you as though you might have been their gipsy queen. In a way you'd 'gone home' to them, hadn't you? Altogether, you inspired me with your strength and commitment to the cause, Ruth.

We were a good team, weren't we? And there were some startling 'results'? Remember the gentle giant who'd been blown to ribbons and could barely drag himself more than a few metres around his home in a district that looked as though it had suffered a nuclear attack? He trusted in Allah. Allah would sort all things. There was no need to worry. The invalid would be well again one day, he assured me. He would *walk*. I gave him healing, to try to ease his pain merely, for about forty minutes. He liked my music tape. He'd not heard anything quite like it before: it was a Christian choral. He lay on his bed, dozing. And when I went to see him the following week his wife, bright-eyed, gesticulating excitedly, led me back up the stairs. I couldn't believe what I saw when I walked into the bedroom.

Let the couple tell the story. That week the patient had been driven by car to a café to see a few friends. He'd had a good time. Then he told the others he felt like having a go at walking home.

'Don't be silly!' his wife had remonstrated with him. 'You can't.'

'I reckon I can.'

'But you're only in your slippers,' she protested.

'So what?' said he.

And he had. It was a slow shuffle, to be sure, but it was true – the wounded man had walked the two kilometres home. He was walking around his bedroom now. He was almost showing off. Oh the smiles. The joy.

Then the man who'd been tortured by the Serbs; they'd cut 'Christian' crosses into his flesh with knives. I was the first male stranger he'd let near him after the war. Where once the touch was hate it was now, I hoped, of love. He wept as I laid my hands on his scars. On the way out, there was a last rose of summer in the shambles of his garden. Just the one. He broke it off and gave it to me. We hugged.

I cried, then.

And last but not least, one of the most beautiful women I had met, ever, coming to greet me at her door and walking like a crab. Part of her face had been blown away. She had a noticeably serene air about her – or was it, I wondered, just shock? When she was receiving the healing her broken countenance was lit with radiance, a smile, unlike any I had known; it was all of it unearthly, and remarked on by the translator. This soul had lost her husband and several of her family and friends in the siege. She herself had been lined up by a sniper on the street and had her head and nervous system shot to pieces. She had hardly any money and her flat was splattered with shrapnel. At the close I wondered whether she would mind my asking her something personal: how had she come by this . . . this, was it, sense of peace? How come she was – happy? She lit up again softly, saying, 'Because my son and I are alive, still. I feel blessed to be here, to have survived. Just that.' Her name: Poturak Zuhra, aged twenty-six. Zuhra reminded me that the butterfly was conspicuous amid the graffiti even upon the walls of Auschwitz.

But then, amidst all this courage and resurrection, you and I blotted our copybooks, or perhaps it would be more accurate to say, I did. We fell out, didn't we, and endured the darkest time I think we'd had, ever. Once more we didn't fight. We looked daggers at the other and slammed bedroom doors on silence instead. *No*, there was going to be no late flowering of romance on this trip. I'd wondered in the margins at one point, as one does sometimes in these cases, whether such might unfold. No chance, though. There were three areas of difficulty.

The first was David. He kept phoning you. No doubt to try to make sure there was no 'late flowering of romance' 'twixt thee and me. Oh God would he please stop *phoning*. He was like a dog who'd lost its owner. I thought you'd come to Sarajevo to be with me, with Healing Hands, with the people who'd suffered in the war. This wasn't a bloody *holiday*, lady.

'Can't you tell your boyfriend to bugger off?' Oh dear. First nail in the coffin.

Next up, our liaison officer, a young Bosnian woman. The house's water supply got cut off and you and I were reduced to scurrying around the neighbourhood at twilight scrounging water in plastic cans from luckier properties. The liaison officer lived in a rather swanky, unbombed apartment downtown and had had an emergency water tank installed but there was no such feature in the clinic. Why not? Surely *that* was a priority? Couldn't she arrange some water for us as an emergency? She couldn't. You and I were reduced to washing our armpits and genitals in pudding bowls of water. We went days without a shower. Patients greeted in stained clothing, with apologies. I got cross with the charity and its representative. You were calmer. In retrospect, you put me to shame.

'John, there's been a war. Stuff doesn't work. We just have to accept these things. There's nothing we can do about it.'

'I'm sorry Ruth, I think there is. I'm going to call home and get this sorted out.'

'The energy you put into all this, what's the point? C'mon . . . '

'The *point* is, it's a matter of principles and practicals, both. We can't do our job properly, face it, in this sort of set-up.'

'Oh, John . . . ' As ever, the dying fall, as if your voice might be giving up on me and despatching itself over a cliff. I suspect I made its owner want to do something similar on occasion. Why you'd opted for (the milksop) David, as you'd said.

'If he phones again I think I'll scream.'

'I thought you came here to do some peaceful healing? Honestly, John. I'm turning in for an early night.'

'Good. Night.'

The trouble didn't stop there did it? On this tour the wretched organisation hadn't even supplied enough interpreters. I was appalled too by the pitifully low pay these vital (and war-impoverished) people were getting, so I took it on myself, no more ado, to hire a good English speaker at a rate three or four times the 'going'. I phoned England and told them. They said, 'You can't do that.' I said, 'I can do whatever I need to, to ensure the service I give these people is professional and safe and doesn't take advantage of the interpreters in the middle.'

'We're not going to pay for this, you know. Nor all these phone calls you keep making.'

'Fine. Then I'll pay for it all out of my own pocket. No water, no interpreters, no bloody understanding – God, what a questionable *charitable* lot you are.' Diplomacy's handmaiden I was, never, as you know.

Next, point four, a member of the executive is hot-footing it to Sarajevo to sort it all out. He has never been here before and his experience of conflict zones, medicine or therapy is zero. How you get to be an 'executive' in the first place of course. As I told you. You continued to roll your eyes like fairground ping-pong balls on fountains.

You go to great lengths to prepare supper for the man who is about to arrive.

'Why are you doing this?' I ask.

'He'll have had a tiring trip and I just think it's an hospitable thing to do. Look I don't feel the same way you do about all this, OK?'

'Anything for the quiet life, hey Ruth? No sticking your neck out, ever.'

'For things I think important, I will. And do. This case I just think you're OTT, that's all.'

'Oh you do, do you?'

'Geoff Dixon is only a volunteer like you and me and I think we can pay him the same respect we would anyone else, no? He hasn't done anything wrong himself, has he?' Your sodding mobile starts jitterbugging. ''Scuse me. Hello? Oh, David, hi. Look I'm really busy just at this moment. I'll call you back, OK? 'Bye.'

'Why don't you and he get married and be done with it, godsake? You can't bear to be five fucking minutes apart.'

'I don't think that's called for.'

I shrug and go start on the beer. By the time Geoff Dixon arrives, late, plane no doubt buzzed and shot at by the fascist Croatians en route, I'm ready for him, a little gimlet-eyed. It is the most awful evening. I tell him I think Healing Hands are a disgrace. He's stiff and tense. You pick at your plate with no appetite. It's an early night all round, and next day we show the exec around Sarajevo. He's gobsmacked by the extent of the damage and the squalor; hasn't a clue. He goes back to England to say or do what I have no idea, and I do not care. I am concerned only with 'the work', and with you.

'I think you were horrible,' is your verdict on the visit. 'I felt sorry for him.'

'As you always are for the lame.'

'That's another thing about you, John. You always have to have the last word. Make sure you stick the stiletto in at the end.'

You had the last word, then. We were wounding each other too much and it was appalling to watch. 'The whole Sarajevo tour become a nightmare,' I jot in my diary. 'One works for the patients, but that's it.' I was going to resign when I got back home, 'begin a new life'. I think I'd written that phrase a few dozen times in diaries over the past thirty years.

'Last day of Bedlam' I scribble as we fly out of the airport, which looks as though it's been hit by a very big bomb.

We were much subdued during the flight home. On the drive up the motorway afterwards we stopped at a service station, and it was a hot September day so we sat on the grass outside. There was distance between us, all ways; we were sitting at an angle away from the other, if not exactly back to back. I turned to you and said I regretted the extent of my anger in Sarajevo but felt I had some cause for it. You went on again about my anger. I said, 'Yes I do get angry, but I'm congruent with it, I express how I feel then, I hope, I let it go. I don't bottle it up.

'I think *you* do that a lot, Ruth.'

You stare bleakly ahead, struggling to find the words that might add something to the moment, not mar it, and for that I honoured you. You picked at grass then threw it away.

'I think you're right,' you said. 'I've been doing it all my life and got used to it. It's how I deal with anything unpleasant. I stuff it away in a box then stick the lid on it. Tightly.'

'You feel angry with me right now for instance, hugely – what happened in Sarajevo there at the end. But you've not once *got* angry.'

'No.'

'But that only means you can never, really, *get real* with me. You've to spend so much of the time *pretending*.'

'Yes. I wish I'd done the PD work you have and had the therapy. Maybe it's time I got started.'

'Maybe. I only know the moment I do get angry with you – about anything – that's it, curtains, we can't take things forward any further. I've lost you. You've fled.'

'Your anger frightens me. I feel I'm "drowning" when you get like that.'

'Can't you see, you're always *drowning* in something, Ruth. Al–ways. Relationships, money problems, other people's anger . . . I dunno. Be nice, no, if you could learn to survive something for once without fear; not least your own anger too?'

'One day.'

'Anger that's not addressed and sorted, it'll get you in the end, Ruth; it'll come and bite you on the bum. You watch.' I paused, full of autumn sadness, knowing soon I'd be depositing you back with David, the other one who 'didn't get angry' either; this pacific pair.

So when I dropped you off we went through the ritual of a perfunctory hug, wished the other rest after the good work we'd put in, but were careful to make no further arrangements. For the next three weeks there's no reference to you in the diary. Then the entry: 'Ruth writes "goodbye".'

Cobblers, of course.

NEW YEAR'S EVE, dusk, and I'm with you still. I'm not going anywhere tonight. A good glass or two of Soave before I eat, that's all. I don't feel lonely. What am I missing? Hordes honking and vomiting, fireworks screaming, the end of our cash-strapped, climate-clapped planet in sight; all of it an hysterical madness. Our age, culture, relationships – all, it would seem, irredeemably adolescent. Like an endless, sickly, bloated feast of popcorn.

What was it Akong had said when I'd started working with him? 'You need to become strong. Resilient. It's important people start preparing themselves for the future.' He'd sounded very gnomic.

'The future . . . what d'you mean?' I'd asked, curious. 'Armageddon? Nuclear holocaust?' (The days, these still, of the Cold War.)

He'd shaken his head. 'No. It'll be worse than that, I would say.' He continued to look impassive; great chunk of basalt rock that he was.

'What on earth could be worse than nuclear holocaust – pffshaw!' I'd puffed.

Eye to eye, no messing, the four stark words: 'Everything, slowly, falling apart.'

'What does *he* know?' a few have scoffed after I've told them what the lama had said. The answer is, I don't know.

Yet as I sit here this evening with my ticking clocks, remembering you frame by frame of the film still, I experience a vestigial peace. You gone now, there's nothing I want save 'the stillness'. Nothing to grieve over, really – your body is gone but what is left is ever beautiful. And at last the 'sign'. I do, I feel you here in the room: *ghost.*

Behind me, arms around my shoulders, nuzzling, you're looking over what I'm writing; you're skittish. You approve, the 'wickedly mischievous' woman you always were. You tell me, 'Write anything and everything. In death I am no longer afraid. Your anger I know was a kind of love, and I know I've been loved by you in a way I was by no other. I'm humbled. I can feel the hints of the tears in your eyes. I'd like to make love to you, but am only a ghost and, I dunno, these days you're maybe past it! It's time I think you went and filled your glass.' I toast the New Year in, 'to both of us', our separate sides of the veil. 'To a better world.'

Is this, again, just the stuff of grief? I don't want to answer phone calls, go anywhere, talk, make arrangements, eat – *live* even? Everything's dead, with you. It's appropriate in a way, we're experiencing a winter that's a perfect match. Day by day as I write, the city and mountains are totally still, and frosted; everything silver or white. Sometimes it's so cold and dead the world beyond my window is consumed by billowing shrouds of fog. At times the skies are afire, colours infernal, as the sun goes down. I merely gaze, type, and love you. I've not seen a soul in a week. I don't mind. I know you are with me, some way. Shall we dance? Yes I could do that, gliding with you across an empty room, man waltzing with a ghost, moving to the music of something soft and slow, and timeless.

YOU WERE, you were just so *sexy*. At Woodlands I used to chase you around the house, no matter that Chris and Robin might be there in their dens plugged into brain damage, so I could play with you; hoisting your dress up smartly and spreading you so I could get to your black gipsy cunt, the other hand rolling pastry with your exquisite bottom, you putting up about as much resistance as a Vichy patsy. You attributed your bouncy absence of sexual inhibition not only to that generous fourteen-year-old apprenticeship but also to your having had a hysterectomy following illness that had freed you from fear of pregnancy. I had never come across a woman able to climax so swiftly and copiously. You were amazing. When you came you looped and kicked like an electric eel and the sounds you made . . . I remember saying once, if the neighbours ever got to hear, they'd be dialling '999'. There was one hilarious occasion I'd been working you with my fingers on the front-room couch. You climbed and climbed. Then you reached orgasm. We heard the door opening and you flung your dress down. I studied my nails. In walks Robin, the permanently starving laddo. 'What's for tea, Mum?' Robin, as ever, in his parallel universe, no idea what's been going on in this one. 'Salmon fishcakes,' I reply, on your behalf. You see, *you're continuing to come*. Couldn't stop, remember? Your knees are knocked together as though trussed with baling twine. Your mouth is tight as a virgin's womb. Your eyes, all over the place. The general effect: France having a fit.

'You all right, Mum?' Rob wonders.

'Mum's fine,' I explain. 'Thinks she's maybe a migraine coming on.' You used to get a few, so it was a plausible alibi.

Trouble was, having to keep your knees clamped like that, to prevent your going berserk at both ends of your body, only made things worse. The harder you squeezed the more interesting the orgasm. I'm sitting there beside you as your flesh works its way through an assorted geometry of convulsions. Carry on like this and we'll have to resort to the fire extinguisher.

Robin's perplexed. He shrugs. 'See Southampton 've got stuffed, then?' He usually gloated when my team lost. I did the same when it happened to Leeds. Just a couple of lads.

'Afraid so.' (God Rob, bog off will you, let your mother *explode* in peace.)

He wanders back upstairs to his all-black bedroom with the Goth-rock and big-tit posters, stinking as ever of socks and wanking. You are able then to collapse all over the settee while I finish you off; you sexually requited and wheezing with laughter in one.

The time, too, we're having sex in the bath and Chris hammers on the door wondering when he might come and have a brush-up as he's going out shortly and 'it sounds,' he says, 'like World War Three in there.'

I would have described it more as 'three-ringed circus' myself.

Good, glad days, and so very brief. This caress of the past.

AFTER THE SARAJEVO boxing match we entered our Dark Ages, hey? A while after we'd been back, there was that meeting in Manchester of the local branch of Healing Hands. I suspected I'd be seeing you there but had got to the point I didn't want any more contact. Fate or whatever seemed to have its own agenda however. I was walking through the streets to the hotel where we were convening and I couldn't believe it – there you were, crossing the road just ahead, coming straight this way. I'd be bumping into you. I had nothing to say. Sadly, for the first time in my life I turned my back on you and returned the way I had come. At the meeting, later, I sat as far away from you as it was possible to get. I griped. I resigned. And then I was sprinting out of the building at the close before there was any chance of our running into the other. It was all of it sad. We had had so much together; now, it seemed, we had nothing left.

The years rolled by, as they do.

I got over you. Or so I thought. I even started a new relationship, glutton for punishment that I was. Fiona was a redhead and red-heads were supposed to be 'fiery' weren't they? And she was 'artistic'. Some combination. So she came with a storm-warning.

Fee had the long auburn locks of a pre-Raphaelite beauty. A researcher in linguistics at the university, M.A. and some public-ations to her name, she had lived and taught in seven countries as far apart as Greece and Indonesia. A conscientious feminist, she brought me to heel sharpish whenever I behaved like a male chauvinist. Skinny as a sixpence, she had little apple breasts and a sweet boy's bum and lived with a fat old tomcat called Oscar. Balls gone, Oscar had got to the point in his life where he made do with cuddles. I was still game for a bit more. Once, after we'd made love, Fiona said she'd enjoyed having her eyelashes sucked, softly. 'No man's ever done that to me before,' she announced, approvingly. Life there was in the old dog yet.

Then, once more, serendipity intervened, as I think it was pretty well bound to in our case, and I turned a sharp corner in the city one lunchtime and banged straight into you.

Blimey.

'Really lovely it was,' I wrote in the diary. It *was*. As though Sarajevo and its sorrows, personal, had never been. We were both excited chatter.

'Fancy a drink?' I wondered.

'Why not?'

Standard greeting format, Pepper and France, as the eavesdropper may be coming to appreciate by this time.

So we went and got gently plastered and caught up on the missing years. No stress, strain, no negative waves of any kind between. You were looking lovely as ever, proverbial bright eyes and bushy tail, not, unbelievably, your fifty-five years at all. I was overjoyed to see you again, so much so that the 'Ruth' in the diary entry is coloured in bright headline orange with a ballpoint-box around and my delight captured, in capitals, by the one word: AMAZING. And, I discover:

- David is gone
- The boys are gone
- The house is gone.

You've started out on a new life, quartered with a womanfriend in a remote valley in the Dales. I wondered if you'd gone lesbian in your old age, but didn't go down that one. Your new set-up sounded promising; the name of the place you were living at was 'Middle Paradise'. You said it was 'the middle of nowhere'.

I don't think very many of us had much idea then but 'the middle of nowhere' was starting to become an accurate description of the direction of your mental state at this time, sadly. However, on the day we crashed into each other I was merely beguiled by your smile, relief there was no longer bad blood between us, and the sunshine, the bliss, of springtime.

THERE ARE A COUPLE of successive link-ups in the May, then June, but you're not at my sixtieth birthday celebration at a country house hotel in Lakeland on the fourteenth. I've invited seven friends closer to me these days than yourself. It's a long weekend of feasting, walking and lazing.

The event, though, is kicked off, as we're sitting with Friday afternoon tea, by the unannounced entrance of a woman carrying the most lavish bunch of flowers I have ever witnessed in my life. It's you. Out of nowhere. Just come to wish me 'Happy Six-O'. I introduce you to one or two people you've not met, Fiona among them. Your turning up like that was a sweet gesture but no, you decline the invitation to linger. You have a drink, then you're off.

I know. You do still care, don't you?

When you leave I come with you, alone, out on to the terrace at the front. I am sorry you are going.

I thought I caught a stray wistful air in you. I didn't know. There was that which was newly enigmatic, I sensed, about you; some-thing that didn't add up. The extraordinarily extravagant nature of your bouquet – that wasn't 'you' was it? Then you'd shot in and out of proceedings like an arrow. Were you upset I'd not invited you in the first place? But Ruth, till a couple of months back, our startled meeting in the street, our friendship had apparently been dead for *years*.

Suddenly I'm all over the place. My partnership with Fiona was gone – we'd ended up as platonic pals after a fling of around a year. Another example I'm afraid of artistic temperaments unable to tango. I wanted you back. I would always 'want you back'. In the 'missing years' I used to hear bits and pieces about you on the grapevine and wander out to fresh villages you'd apparently ended up in, and I'd prowl around the addresses I'd managed to pick up, hoping to God you'd not find me nosing around, yet praying that you might. I would creep up to cottage windowpanes and peer in ever so tentatively, like a mischievous child. I never caught sight of you once. I'd drive back home, flat, disappointed, sometimes castigating myself: 'What d'you think you're *doin*', Pepper? Hey? Gawd!' Stalker, I couldn't help it. The trail on you and your life had gone cold, that's all.

And yet here we are again, lass, back together in some way. What now? I don't think either of us had a clue. On the terrace we linger.

'What's wrong, Ruth?' I could tell something was. My intuition had always been something I'd prized. It was working well here, though I hadn't picked this up when we'd had the chance encounter and gone to the pub. Then you'd been all light and dancing. Here there's a small shadow over your heart.

'Wrong?' you swerve, startled. 'Wrong with what?'

'Things generally. They aren't all they might seem, are they? In your life . . . '

'I'm struggling a bit.' And immediately looking anxious.

I loop my arm around you and draw you close. Whatever I do to, with or for you always seems to me, on one level, the most natural, uncomplicated thing in the world. 'Why, what's going on?'

You sighed. 'Oh it's at work. My line manager's got it in for me, I think. Doesn't like me.'

'Why ever not?'

'I think I threaten her in some way. My experience, and then having been married to Jim.'

Your 'ex', then, was still one of the big wheels in social services? Yes he was. Managing half the county's provision.

'Another bloody day at the office, hey?' I sympathise. It's a lacklustre June afternoon; dark, damp, a storm on the way. I hug you all the more, to warm you.

'She's always pulling me up on my work these days,' you go on. 'I can't do right from wrong.'

'Can't you sort it? Smack her on the nose or something?'

You laugh. 'I wouldn't mind sometimes.'

'What are you doing to help yourself, anyhow?' I want to know. I'm concerned about you.

'I've had a bit of counselling. It's a doctor who does some. A woman.'

'Is it helping?'

'I think so.' You sound underwhelmed. Here I have my own agenda sticking its nose over the parapet. Doctors by definition didn't make 'the best' counsellors, usually. They were too acculturised to their medical model of working: *the doctor knows best*. The expert. Counselling traditionally was more about mutuality, the development of deep therapeutic relationship. So I sniffed, a fraction.

'Look after yourself,' I urged while you said you'd better be on your way.

And, alas, that was the one thing you did not do. From around this time it was all quietly downhill I suppose to the river, apart from that last glad, golden year and the few times before when you did glimmer enchantingly, summer light flickering through the leaves, as the beauty that was Ruth France struggled with the beast.

New Year's Eve, suddenly it comes to me. That autumn I'd lent you two thousand quid at a go to stop you flogging your car, something you were actively seeking to do, desperate for lolly as you were. I reckoned that without wheels you'd find life pretty constricting in the little Book Town you'd finally, by this time, ended up in, in, again, 'the middle of nowhere'. I lent you the cash so you could keep the car. I should've let you sell up. My kindness might not then have killed you. You wouldn't have ventured out that final fatal evening if all you'd had was a bike.

Reflection as New Year dawns, and I kiss you goodnight.

YOU'D LOST SO MUCH so quickly. From this point on you wandered through your life wondering what to do with it. Now you were no longer a wife, active mother, householder, lover or up close and personal with anyone, and retirement was a discernible landmark on the horizon in your work, I think you struggled. You were losing your labels. You were starting to be free but, as Sartre said, '*Freedom is terror.*'

For so many it is, I know. We prefer to live in chains. (In the police force I worked with as a counsellor, the common phrase for the thirty-year job security officers enjoyed was 'the golden hand-cuffs'. The hearty pension was all. And often a killer). Found it so difficult to live lives in the moment, didn't we, and let the future look after itself? Back then to Leunig's 'fear': I began to sense that in the last few years of your life the contest between the love and the fear was battle royal. It was one though the love that was richly Ruth France was winning slowly. And regally, indeed, at the close. Your end was triumph and disaster, both.

I piece it together that the rot began not when the boys flew – I think you would have come to terms with the natural order of that one – but when you quit that lovely old home of twenty years by the river, and the manner in which you did so. Chris gone, Rob heading that way, your 'ex' Jim wanted to come back there. Make the house his own. He'd finished his tenure with the schoolmistress and was in a new relationship. He was going to re-marry. When he did so, in May 1996, I wrote to him with my good wishes, in keeping with the good-hearted relationship I think I'd always enjoyed with him. I didn't know who his new wife was.

It transpired she was Corinne, *your boss*, your nemesis at the office, now to be installed as mistress of the house that had been the heartbeat of the happiest years of your life.

The pain of it all, I think, cut you to ribbons. You fled in such disorder you made no serious financial and legal provision for yourself, did you? You just 'got out'. Like a driven figure in a Hardy novel you began your lonely wanderings around those rented hides in the backwoods, and would never return to that beautiful old house again.

I went to pick Rob up there on one occasion and it hurt me, too, to have the door opened on me, once more, by a stranger and make stilted small-talk with the new mistress of Woodlands, Robin perched awkwardly to one side on one leg like one of the herons down on the estuary.

As had happened with my meeting David for the first time, though, afterwards I couldn't remember a thing about Corinne; how she looked, what she said or did. She was a bit stiff and polite, that's all I retained. Somehow unhappiness obliterates the detail of so many things – echoes of electroconvulsive therapy, ECT.

At this time we were a little way from that one yet, but the rot was in.

I used to sit and have coffee with you, or we'd go for little walks together through winter woods and fields, the imprints of which we would never remember, either, as the bleakness of your interior world unfolded. Yes, David had left, but by this time I wasn't triumphal; I let you offload and I listened. He was set up with another woman and, as he had with you, he was living off her. Or so you claimed. He'd tried to get you to go back with him but you'd driven him off. There was discernible anger in you these days. Cordite sniffs of wrath; you slung some ripe language at the guy.

I asked whether you ever used to talk about me like that, after we'd split. You said you didn't. I had no way of knowing whether you were telling the truth. You were in a dark, windblown place. I'd never seen you quite like this before.

Or had I? What about our first real meeting, our *Brief Encounter* at the station, when you'd wheeled away from my hug in the night with tears unstilled and that terrible cry in your throat?

But let's set the record straight: even while the shadow France was emerging like some rough beast from the underworld, the sunshine shone still. Of course it did. My Aunt Joan met you just the once and told me you were one of the most beautiful women she'd ever come across. You and my mother both – to whom in time I'd come to realise you bore a certain resemblance, of course; those 'lost and distant' reminders I'd experienced, inchoately, when I'd met you first. I should take you off, Joan said, and marry you forthwith. The pair of you did get on. Joan I took a lot of notice of; she was one of the kindest and wisest souls I had known. When the bombs were falling in the war and my mother was a wreck, Joan, her best friend (she was never really my 'aunt'), calm and light, would often look after me instead. She became a second mother to me. She still lived in that 'dreary Northern town' I'd been born in and ultimately fled, skipping, joy in my heart. Joan was stability personified. Didn't have a bad word to say about anyone, did she? I know you were much taken with her; you formed an instant bond. But I couldn't 'take you off and marry you', could I? I remained wary of you, a bit. 'Marriage', a lot.

Still, as friends reunited we did enjoy our pocket corner of England, so much off the beaten track still, unknown to many and prized therefore by the few. It's a special place and I shall always love *her*, too. There was one reach of lake we both treasured particularly. Look up behind you into the woods and crags this side, across to the forests and mountains on the other, then left and right along the water, and it's wilderness all the way. No house, boat-house, jetty, buoy, lamp. Nothing. And all this an hour from our doors. It was there with you, on that pocket-handkerchief beach of rough pebbles, I used to feel I'd won more than the lottery; I'd come by 'the answer'. This, the beauty I aspired to live by, within myself and without, all the way to the end. Ruth France beside me among the wild flowers and bright blue damselflies, birds calling, the sun going down on the water in a shattering of gold – what *more*? Sometimes I dreamed of setting up a bothy on the beach and writing a novel just about the quiet that fell on the lake in the evening after everyone had gone home and it was left to itself. In that peace lay *all* we needed.

If I'd had the chance, the courage, the freedom from cynicism and the money, I wouldn't have minded being married to you right there in the springtime, spending the night with thee among the bluebells we once looked out for everywhere we went so we could hunker down and make love among them. An incurable pair of romantics. Kids with crows' feet.

Remember how I used to swim across the lake to the other side or lounge around on my back in the middle, skirted by yachtsmen who'd sometimes lean over their gunwhales, a touch worried, to enquire if I was 'alright?' – 'Alright? I'm in bliss, sir!' – and stay out for ages while you kept resolutely to your lounger on the shore, shuddering at the very sight of me splashing around in the 'deep, dark' waters of your nightmares.

Even in home waters, no, I *couldn't* tempt you in for a swim, could I? I think you once went in up to your ankles for fifteen seconds. Must have been an horrendously hot day.

'What you need to remember, John,' you joked with me once, 'this thing about water and me is so huge and irrational, I could even get to be scared by a birdbath.'

In such contrast to yourself I had loved water all my life, as you knew. I was a wild-swimming madman, wasn't I? I used to count the number of swims I managed in rivers, lakes and the sea each summer, and try every time to beat the previous year's tally. A couple of years back, the record then, I'd managed forty-three. I was a good swimmer; I had no fear. But I was sensible. To me the most exhilarating experience in life beyond making love to the likes of you, watching the dawn light in the eye of those working through their travails and griefs, and healing, is swimming towards the last sun as it falls in the water of ocean or lake. I half-close my eyes and swim through the fireflies of light on each wavelet so my mind fills with the kind of radiance they say you arrive at, reaching the end of the tunnel, as you die. I pray you may have seen such, as the waters closed over you.

So indeed, we made merry even as you were starting to come apart. 'Pure heaven of a day' was one I noted in my writing once. Yet hell was just around the corner, hey?

EVENTUALLY I COME TO SEE YOU in 'Middle Paradise'. Wander-woman has been taken under Jackie's wing after the two of you had met for the first time at the meditation centre in the valley in which you are going to drown. At that point Jackie was holed up in another valley so remote I wondered whether 'Paradise' was the best place for you. J, the busy landowner, eco-campaigner and red squirrel protector, with family and friends around the world, is often absent. You're left then on your own, with the mutt Sara and the cats. You say you like the peace but I can pick up your loneliness. Unease. I feel I'm 'losing you', all ways. You're not 'with me'; Ruth, you're not well.

I notice, for the first time, the unpleasant smell of your breath.

I think you need more than counselling. Long-term psycho-therapy, I would say. Whatever – you need help of some sort. You're like an engine revving that's not in gear. You're in danger, I think, of blowing up.

The anger you feel towards Jim, Corinne, David, your brother and sister and others is piling up inside you like distant rolls of thunder. I'm frightened for you.

You allege you're being 'treated rotten' at work. You don't like what the place has become. You've nowhere to live except here at Jackie's. Nothing, really, left at all.

'Except yourself, Ruth, and all the goodness and beauty you are despite what's happening to you,' I insist. 'And don't forget you've the boys – the credits to you 'specially they've turned out to be.'

'They don't need me any more.'

'No of course they don't *need* you, they just love you. Very much: I know that to be a fact. And so do all your friends; the large number of them.'

'I'm letting everyone down,' you mourn.

'You can't let down those who love you, Ruth. Love that can be let down isn't love – it's horseshit. Trade. So there's nothing you can do to rubbish the love of those who really do so. You can't carve up love like that. It's as hard and bright as a diamond. Love that's love, the real thing, it's indestructible. The best definition of love there is, I reckon.'

'I feel so unwell,' you crumble, starts of tears in your eyes.

So Jackie does more for you. She puts you up in your own place, a cottage she has in the village in the next valley where there'll be more people around you. You come and see me in the city and I'm shocked by what arrives at my door; the sour cheese of your flesh and dirty dangle of your hair. Your clothes are stained with food and heaven knows what else, your fingernails ripped and bleeding. Your walk is a shuffle. You stink. You find it difficult to look me in the eye. I want to hold you close and protect you from all that hurts you.

Jackie goes on giving to you; now she offers to set you up in your first proper home of your own since you'd fled Woodlands all those years ago. She would buy half a flat for you if you could raise a mortgage on the other half. You'd share ownership. The universe was continuing to look after you, as you noted, yourself. You found a small flat opening on to a quiet communal garden in a new block among the trees and hills of the little town, that Book Town (not much more than a village, really) at the end of the vale you'd fallen in love with, all bare tops and lush bottoms with that meditation centre at its heart. After your long wanderings and travails it was a haven, backing music from a tiny brook, the kind of water you *didn't* mind. You walked out of the grounds and right away were on a steep hill leading up to a range of them that roamed waves of clouds like whales. It was all of it peaceful and pretty. On a soft spring day you invited me 'to be my first guest' in your new home. I was so pleased for you. I was also quietly worried.

You were still not yourself.

Down in the deepest part of you there was no *quiet*. There was plenty of it around you in your leafy redoubt but I couldn't make contact with very much in your heart. You admitted you didn't find it easy living on your own. Made you feel queasy sometimes. I think it always did, Ruth. You'd always lived with others since you were a very young woman through to the time Rob, as a young man, went off to his new life in Leeds. You'd never cultivated solitude as one cultivates a garden. It was a wild place largely unexplored, peopled still on winter's days with ghosts. You'd begun hacking through some of the undergrowth with your meditations, but only haphazardly, intermittently, as so many people do when they meditate as a means to get a little breath back in the battle of life rather than to change their breathing altogether, their *experiencing*, and thereby transform their minds. You stacked dime-store Buddhas and religious icons around the flat as replacements, I think, for the real thing; the focused *work* sorely needed now, surely, as your life started to split asunder?

You went back to Bosnia on your own, Mostar this time, as the best part of you flowered again for a while and sought to help others. You reported on the festering hatred that existed still between communities divided by that famous arching bridge over waters which, a few years back, had been racing with corpses and blood. You massaged your way back to a modicum of health. I heard, again, you'd done a magnificent job; you were a genuine magician with your hands. When you returned, you looked good.

I wondered, way after your death, whether you'd lied to me about going back to Bosnia alone. When Chris showed me some of the old photographs you'd left, there was one of you and a handsome chap at a café in what looked to me like the Balkans. It could have been someplace other than Bosnia. Maybe.

'Who's the good-looking feller with your mum here?' I'd asked Chris.

'Oh, that's David,' he said.

I didn't pursue the matter further.

Back home, you kept going at work. 'Kept going' the operative words. It wasn't a happy run-down to a distinguished career, was it? To your clients, the children and their guardians, I know you still gave your best, but to the service and its apparatchiks you gave out a lot of shaking of the head. You felt let down. Alone. Misunderstood.

Paranoid, even? Were these tales of 'the terrible other' true, all of them? I didn't know what was going on, Ruth. My task was but to listen to you, one-sided, and love, bearing constant witness to my own transgressions when it came to 'staying awake'. I could be a miserabilist too, an acid critic. My 'kindness' still struggled sometimes with a world I was increasingly less than enamoured with and from which we both spoke increasingly of our desire to flee, as though there might be somewhere else on the planet we might sensibly depart to other than a reconstituted realm inside ourselves. Still, it was nice to dream together of Utopia, as we did. Lunatic, though.

And it was at this point that lunacy struck. Hard. The moment that changed everything.

CHRIS AND HIS GIRLFRIEND LURA were looking after you for a while at their home in one of your 'wobbles'. In Chris's own words, 'Mum locked herself away for a couple of months in her room and I started to think something was wrong. She was drinking too much and tried to hide the evidence under her bed – we found a hoard of empty bottles there later. Gin, mainly. Anyway, one day she phoned me at work saying, "I need to talk to you." When I arrived I found her a bit weird, clearly disoriented. We sat down on her bed to talk. She said "nothing's wrong," but then grabbed my glasses and threw them across the room. She said, "I'm sorry. Your face changed."

'Next she snatched at a security badge on my belt and tore it off. I said, "I'm going to call the hospital," and while I was on the phone she came at me brandishing a knife. I just grabbed it off her, parked her on the bed and rang the police. Although it was only a table knife, I was frightened and ran out of the house and waited for the police to come.

'When we went in, Mum had taken all her clothes off. She was perfectly calm. The police got her clothed and took her away. On the way to the police station Mum then attacked a policewoman in the van.'

And that was how you were put away in a psychiatric ward; the woman who was, in the words of your admirers, 'one in a million', 'a very special person' and 'one of the most caring and compassionate souls I have known'. 'She will,' it was said, 'make a great angel.'

At this moment alas she was, all too human, in domains of almost unimaginable dark. Beloved Ruth, where are you?

Who are you?

YOU DON'T TRY to hide what happened. But the detail of that

dreadful hour you can't remember afterwards. It had all been a blur; you were off your head. A 'psychotic episode', it would appear. It was as if a lifetime of molten rage that had lain dormant within you had suddenly erupted like a volcano. It had been a spectacular, horrid, show.

Now you lowered and shook your head with shame. Remorse.

After a while you're transferred to a hospital nearer home, the notorious local 'Ward Four'. You describe the place as being 'full of crazies'. They frighten you. There's no one there with whom you can make any meaningful contact. You're being stuffed with yet more antidepressant drugs, and given ECT.

You've had, I think, two encounters with the voodoo voltage when I see you in the waiting room outside the ward. They're letting you out for a couple of hours so we can walk and have a coffee. You're scruffy and quiet. Somehow all the life in you has been blown away like the petals off a flower. What's left is the stalk.

I walk with you in the drizzle, fighting to hold back my tears.

No it didn't hurt, the ECT. You don't mind it; they say it's the best thing for you. Your depression's bad. You have no idea how long they're going to keep you in there. *Weeks*?

Is there anything I can do for you or get you? Anything at all?

Not really.

I'm taken back to the days long ago when I was in a similar set-up but without the ECT, instead a chemical cosh of largactil, my world fallen apart and all the love and friendship that existed in it for me insufficient still to quell my fear, the feeling that I wasn't worthy of another's love because I always failed to keep it. And I was so angry towards those who had taken it away, even if they'd had their 'reasons'. I think you and I tried so hard to win the love of others we let slip the fundamental law that the most important love of all *was* the one we reserved for ourselves. No, not narcissism, egoic self-love, but the love we bore for the spirit within us.

'And how would you define that then?' you would have me decipher for you there in the stuffy, misty-window, child-screaming stew of a bog-standard English tea shop on a wet afternoon. You were always inquisitive, France, even with half your brain shot out and your knickers, you know that, showing over the top of your trousers. 'Spirit'? – like it was a simple question in a TV quiz show.

'Maybe – I dunno – maybe just the tenderness of heart, the humility, which accepts it knows nothing very much and enables you to live in awe and wonder, and general goodwill, care, for the best part of your days. Ever so simply, perhaps just what's the best in us. Something like that.'

You're reasonably satisfied, and eat your carrot cake and sip your cappuccino like a good girl. Bit of me at this point, I have to acknowledge, was wishing that you might have felt more like *screaming*, lobbing a table through the plate-glass window, say, or setting about Jim France with an axe. What we have here isn't 'remedy', or 'peace'. It's human blancmange.

Anyway, I don't bonk you or get you drunk and return you to the ward in the small hours with a helium balloon pinned to your bottom. Something in me would have liked to have done that too. This wasn't processing your anger, finding out its importance and meaning for you and what you might serviceably do to recycle its vast resources of energy into something more productive. (As Akong once said to me, *praising* my anger, 'Value it. It's fuel. It can take you a long way. Learn to transmute it into compassion instead.') No, electroconvulsive therapy did nothing to help you understand your anger or yourself. It simply flattened you, like a nuclear bomb. Great, win the war. Then what do you do with the fried zombie who's left?

As I said goodnight to you, big hug in the sterile antechamber of your madhouse, how could I tell you in a way that would make any difference that depression and rage, once my scourge, had become the friends spearheading my healing and the happiness increasingly my gift? How could I save you from a system of medicine that saw everything as a 'battle against' rather than a 'deep understanding of', for it was not 'fight' that would save you now, it was one thing only: love.

I left you, howling my way through the car park, rage of my own, OK, as well as the weeping. Sometimes anger was the right response to things. Kill it, Ruth, at your peril. As you'd tried to do all your life with the consequences you were experiencing right now on your ward of broken hopes and dreams.

You've had half a dozen sessions of the ECT; I find you like a bird with broken wings, flapping around but unable to fly. I wonder: can you ever again be the Ruth I've known and loved so long? Or are you changed, for the worse, forever?

I think you have finally understood that the person who was most angry in our relationship wasn't me; it was you. My anger rubbed against the edges of your own and scared you. Your rage was vast and unaddressed. It hid away in you in deep deposits of depression, coming to light only in your breakdown; the knife attack on your son, finally, which said it all.

Unbeknown to me, things get worse. In a grotesque precursor of the death to come, you've shuffled on foot to the river down the road from the hospital. You've taken an overdose of hoarded aspirin.

You wade into the water to die. You can see no further point in living. You've had enough. You drowned in your last life; you want to drown in this one.

The water lapping your thighs, you stop, pause, and stumble back to the bank. Chris told me afterwards, 'She said she was thinking about Rob and me, and in the end she just couldn't do it because she knew it would cause us so much pain.'

I knew nothing of any of it till after your death.

BIT BY BIT you do get better and eventually go home. Yet Chris admitted, 'Things still weren't right. I remember one time she wanted a beer at seven o'clock in the morning.'

In the meantime your next escape route from things is sex.

Knowing you, I wasn't surprised. Again, it wasn't with me, it was with – let's call this one, 'Desmond'. I can't remember how you came to meet him but you'd done so somewhere and now you were seeing each other, largely in bed. Many ways it was a touching story. Desmond's wife had multiple sclerosis and the point had come where she was incapable of engaging in a sex life any longer. She'd been gracious, and said to her husband: 'Look let me be plain, Desmond' – as he told you then you told me, as one does – 'if you go off and have a sexual relationship with somebody, that'd be fine by me. I can't expect you to stay at home and nurse me like you do and be celibate the rest of your life. So if you wish to – go, find someone.' And Desmond had done so and the gods had smiled on him, France. He found you.

'I do need sex,' you'd told me at this time. Straight to the point on this subject at least (oh yes, you are 'getting better'). 'It's an important part of me. The touch, intimacy – the works. I'm still as keen as I used to be.' I nodded a little, like the pro I am. These days sex for me is like an old sepia photograph. Another age. But I'm happy to listen, as I do.

'And it's a good relationship, sexually. That's all it is, mind. Sex.'

'Is that enough?' I enquire, shocked and righteous in one. Truth is at this time I'm asking myself: do *I* still fancy you? Not sure. I have such glitzy memories of our sexual Golden Age but do sit here feeling frazzled by all you and I have been through, and you're starting to get a bit overweight and jowly these days aren't you, and, well, I'm just not sure. May–be. But it's irrelevant anyway. You are bonking Desmond.

'Not normally it wouldn't be, no, of course not. In the real thing I'd need a lot more,' you wish me to understand. 'But it isn't that sort of arrangement. At all. It is just sex. We meet about once a week or so, take our clothes off, and that's it.'

OK. Please, spare me the details, France. Mercifully, you do.

'Well I wish you luck,' I offer, as though you're about to shoot off to bingo, or the races.

'Thank you. He's not even good-looking. Desmond, I mean. Very ordinary really. And bald.' I wonder if you're having a late re-think but go on sipping my wine and looking sagacious even if there is a very long way to go yet before I dare call myself 'sage'.

'That doesn't matter,' I continue kindly, though in a quickfire analysis of my own sexual history I know that's an unholy lie; I've never been to bed with an ugly woman in my life. They've all been crackers (more ways than one, sometimes).

'No it doesn't,' you say loudly, as if to convince yourself. 'But he is very kind. An old-fashioned gentleman, sort of. He is *nice*. And I am fond of him.'

'That helps,' I come in snappily, with the suggestion of an edge. I don't want to hear all this stuff about yet another guy in your knickers.

By rights that was always my abode.

Let me look at that one, shall I? I did so on the spot, fishing up a slightly toxic mix of resentment, rage, regret and many other things, apropos France, I am sure I could think of beginning with 'r'. In a nutshell, I *continue* on some level to feel hurt by you. I'm another wounded infantryman in love's wars. (More than 'wounded', Pepper, face it. Shot-to-pieces, more like.)

'Maybe,' you say, 'I can introduce you sometime.'

I'd like to say *I'm in no hurry* but don't want to sound peevish. Doesn't help anybody. Doesn't do a lot for my credibility as some-one who's written books with titles like *How To Be Happy* and

Seeing The Light. I've a lot to live up to. Must behave myself. So I say, 'U-huh.'

You're sensitive enough to take that one no further. Though you're not done with Desmond yet, or rather, with sex, because you turn on me then and ask point-blank where I am in my sex life these days, your head tilted a tiny degree to one side then to the other as though juggling tease and genuine curiosity – to which would I prefer to respond? Neither, though I do offer up a 'harrumph!' like a release of wind from indigestion, then smirk, '*What* sex?'

'Bad as that is it? Oh dear.' You are, you are genuinely concerned, as ever. 'I thought you liked Fiona. So it's not *working*, then?'

'Not 'specially. Not any longer as a partnership, anyway. We've stayed friends though.' That seems my allotted role in life doesn't it? 'Good friend'.

Sexual failure?

Don't like the look or sound of that one, so direct the traffic back to Desmond whom I can't get out of my mind as a man in white shirt-tails and no trousers with bandy legs wandering around your bed with a big bald head. He's frozen in time for me there. I mustn't take him seriously. The last suitor I took 'seriously', His Holiness the Serene David, did me a terrible amount of emotional damage I am determined shall not be repeated. Any other man in your life henceforth is going to be turned into a cartoon. Remember, I became a cartoonist in the first place as a kid deflecting the pain of the bullying I'd started to get in the school playground because a) I was quite small and b) had a funny Northern accent – my family had moved down to Southampton where everyone there, sloppy-mouthed Southerners, sounded as though *they* were whining on about their haemorrhoids. In the end I made other boys laugh and saved my skin. Desmond is going to be turned into a joke likewise.

'Desmond – if he's no hair, he's bald you say, when you're shagging him what d'you hang on to then? His ears?'

But you're not going to be deflected, are you, now you're on your favourite subject. You wave my whimsy aside. 'So if it's all over with Fiona, the sex I mean, what d'you do about sex these days?'

'You know I'm very influenced by Zen and you've heard the koan, about The Sound of One Hand Clapping.' I am then silent. Quietly enigmatic.

You giggle, but then go straight-faced again and come over all marriage guidance counsellor on me. 'Oh that's sad. How long are you going to go on like that, John?'

'Depends how well the Hand goes on Clapping, I s'pose . . . '

'I'm serious!' you protest. Your huge inquisitiveness about the world was commented on by so many in your life; you always wanted to *know*, didn't you? 'You're not going to be celibate the rest of your life are you!' The prospect made you look ill.

'I dunno,' said I. There stood truth unvarnished.

'That'd be such a shame,' you murmur. So you remember the good times do you? They were, weren't they? Once you said to me, simply, no tambourines and trumpets, that our sex had been the best you'd had in your life. Same, my way. Now you've having loveless humps with a baldie and I'm left with DIY. Doesn't sound, feel, fair. The ruin, hey, that is 'growing old'?

Yet I *was* happy for you that Desmond was making you a little happier and I didn't feel jealousy towards him. Alright – pause, Pepper – a twinge, but nothing of note. Perhaps growing older had its good things too.

What the affair with Desmond did result in, however, was the beginning of yet another period of separation between us. You didn't 'just' go to bed with Desmond, eventually. You went out for meals, to movies, theatre and on walks with him. On one occasion I was with a friend and caught up with the two of you at the Lowry in Manchester, where your 'hero' Tony Benn was talking. We sat with you and shared a drink. You were right, Desmond was a sweet guy. When the show was over I waved the two of you off, feeling alright. Just a small lingering perfume of sadness. What I wished you, though, was real. As the Bard might've put it, here: 'Go to, girl. Go to.'

Until such time it is fade, our lives no longer touching once more.

MULLED SHIRAZ and sherried bread and butter pudding by the roaring log fire, and a spangled-mist trawl together along the lakeside and back. Perfect start to another year, exactly five years ago today.

One or other of us must've phoned the other and said, 'Hi, long time, no see. How about a New Year drink?' It felt like a 'right time' to re-connect, see where we might be with each other. I did *miss* you. Without you something in my life 'wasn't quite right', ever.

What *was* that? Ah . . . got it: above all I think it was that sense of fun. You were up for anything, really. Daft idea? 'Fine.' Not sure about this one, hmm . . . what d'you think? 'Let's try it.' I'm a bit concerned here, if I'm honest. 'Sounds like a really great challenge to me.' I know what it is: you didn't go on like so much of the rest of the world does, saying *no*. You were a *yes* woman in the very best sense of the word. I rose to that devil-may-care in you – such stark contradiction, *strange*, to your fears say around anger, or water? At our best you and I were naughty boys and girls. We weren't worried what the neighbours might think. What at our age we 'should' do. I liked the tattoo on your shoulder. Your thongs. The porn videos. And your *courage*, lest we forget. The evening at the cinema when the movie had been wrecked by yobs at the back braying and rioting, as they do. You'd been patience personified, Rob recounted (to the throng at your funeral), till you'd finally snapped. (Hurray! Ruth gets angry!) And what does 'sweet Ruth' do? She goes and grabs the lead hoodie by the throat, carts him out of the studio, and dumps him at the desk. 'Deal with him!' she orders. *Now that's my Ruth*.

The New Year starts my end, then, not only with a new phase with you but with a new home also. That imposing old Victorian flat amid the trees and flowers in which you and I had shared so much love and laughter had been thieved by a judge. I thought I had security of tenure in law, as lawyers insisted I had, but new landlords, millionaires, wanted me out so they could develop the entire house and make yet more money. Why am I not surprised?

They took me to court and won, as you know. The judge took no notice of the fact that Number Two had been my home for more than seventeen years. He gave me twenty-eight days to wrap up my life and get out. I was homeless. I put all my furniture and possessions into storage and went to live with friends. For six months I moved around spare beds. You offered me yours, remember? I thought, 'Hmm, better not.' We might, just might, end up having some sex again and, gulp, where might that leave us? Besides, you were nicely oiled and up and running with Desmond; sexually, I was an old wreck. I think I feared I might be a terrible disappointment in bed for you after all these years, and the sadness both ways to which that might give rise. I lacked courage, or was it that I showed wisdom? Not sure. So, no, I didn't come and spend my nights divided by a thin partition from your big white bed and drawers full of sexy smalls. I went to platonic pals, Brenda's and Fiona's, and got lots of serious reading done in bed instead.

Who knows how our lives might have turned out had I decided, as they say, to 'go for it, brother'. Might you still be alive today?

The universe was looking after me as well, though, and I found myself with a new home in the sky. It remains as intoxicatingly attractive for me today as on the day when, to my amazement and excitement, I was offered it by a friend; my high, modern, all-white eyrie below which city and sea, entire, extend in a frieze. It's the perfect 'far away' place for counselling and writing, isn't it? With the striking, brightly coloured abstract and impressionist paintings I've collected on its walls, you said it looked like an art gallery. Nearly the whole of the front of my living room, flooding me with light, is glass. The place is kept cosy with the underfloor heating. There's that wide field of waving grass immediately to the front and a fox, owl and woodpecker wood at the back. I can walk, however, into the centre of the city in about quarter of an hour. In my bedroom I sit on summer evenings looking across to the hills in which I'd spent my nine solitary winters looking for meaning, searching for self. And here in the simplicity and quiet of a new home I begin, I think, to harvest the fruits. Does, it feels, again, like a 'coming home'.

Akong nods and smiles and clicks his beads. I'd been meditating now, nearly every day that passed, in the same meditation practice, for over a quarter of a century. I sat and 'did nothing' to the benefit, ultimately, I believe, of everything I was and did. Half an hour of peace. It was a popular Tibetan exercise where one visualised oneself as Chenrezig, 'deity of compassion'. He was white, crowned, dressed in sumptuous robes, with a rosary in one hand representing wisdom, and a flower, symbol of compassion, in the other. Wisdom and compassion the foundations of 'the good life', in every sense.

Chenrezig wore a look of immense solicitude. The Tibetans didn't think of the guy as a 'god' in the sense we might; Chenrezig was a manifestation of the mind. Deities were seen as kaleido-scopic facets of it, and not just 'my' mind but the universe's too. The 'soup' containing everyone and everything. In time, as the mind grows more still, focused resolutely on the 'deity', the figure begins to dissolve. It turns into light. Thoughts pass by like wisps of cloud and the light burns them off. With good practice the mind could become very quiet. The body, still. The theory: bit by bit the practitioner would by dint of their subtle 'marination' in Chenrezig's qualities start to find themselves increasingly invested with them also. 'A psychological conjuring trick,' wrote one celebrated explorer of the system. 'It would not be surprising if psychiatrists were to castigate it as a sure way to insanity; yet Tibetans, almost every one of whom cherishes a "deity", are by and large a people eminently sane and free from the stresses and complexes that wreak such havoc among the peoples of the modern world.' Nevertheless, reaching 'Nirvana', the moment where the mind stopped dividing the world up into fragments, all boundaries finally eclipsing into the ultimate, 'cosmic', consciousness – what I liked to call the point where the contradictions of a paradox meet – as with any other serious method of psychological healing invariably took the individual through hell and high water on the way as they explored the undertows of their neuroses and ailments.

You and I had certainly experienced the 'deep, dark' truths of that one, hadn't we? Our lives had whirled like rafts on stormy seas. But the storms were starting to quieten now and the peace you were to come to experience at the end was the just reward, ultimately, of your dedicated voyage through them. I think my gift of Chenrezig was 'the best' I ever gave you. At long last you started to meditate 'properly'; that's to say, with serious focus, consistently. And you were sitting in Chenrezig's light in the meditation centre, the morning of your death.

But we're jumping ahead. There were other convulsions to come. Yet more.

FOR NOW, THOUGH, with our two spanking-new homes, one in the city, the other in the country, I with plenty of work and you thinking of packing yours in, and spring on the way, we seemed to have come to a new, glad place together. Remember the screaming fun we had setting up in my apartment, when trying to assemble flat-pack furnishings had the pair of us, well, *screaming*? Have more Allen keys been hurled around four walls in history? More crap slabs of hardboard, crumbled? More lopsided items of furniture erected? The only way we could deal with it was to collapse into laughter and afterwards go down the pub and sink some. Neither of us had 'any idea', did we? In matters practical we were useless. However, I think we were quietly proud of the fact. It gave us lots of time otherwise to 'do nothing, well'.

So I loved driving up to the soft hills to see you now and I know you used to rev up when you dropped down to the city. Again we had the best of both worlds, and I got to thinking 'This is nigh perfect. Both of us, as ever, skint most of the time yet we've two superb homes in such contrasting places in the loveliest corner in the land.' We had lots of friends, and inner lives we cherished, sharing the same ideals and aspirations. We believed in lives of care-and-share, but for possessions, by and large, other than books and paintings, we cared nothing. We *did* like fun, though.

This springtime, seated for the first time at my window, surveying the glory of my inheritance out there beneath the finest sunsets in England, I thought I had it 'made'. In what was the first time in a long while I got to thinking, idly I have to admit, yet fairly frequently, and conscious still of Desmond's involvement in your life, whether there might be any mileage in our somehow formalising a 'getting back together' again, becoming one of those new couples choosing to 'live apart but be together', perhaps. I had pictures in my mind of a big party under the dome of the memorial by the butterfly house up the road, and you and I pledging ourselves to the other, formally, in front of our friends. Something of that ilk anyway.

Fear held me back. What if you said no? What if you said yes, and the whole thing turned out to be a horrible disaster after all we'd been through *as it was*? How the heck would I be able to deal with, and survive, that one?

As it was, the way I was 'surviving' in my emotional life was canny; it might have been called spreading your bets. Eschewing messy partnerships, I'd gathered quite a high number of *platonic* womenfriends around me instead; my 'harem' as one or two of my (bemused) male friends used to joke. They were special people, all. I might not be much good at keeping a marriage or a relationship going, but it was evident I *did* have the gift of friendship. Friends had become my family in the absence of my having a real one. Let it be said I didn't gather my womenfriends around me with the express intention of my so doing but, in time, I came to appreciate that what I'd done unconsciously was set up insurance against my being ever crushed with hurt again. A platonic friend might move away, tire of the friendship, die even, and I'd be saddened, but I wouldn't go away again wanting the earth to swallow me. If I had a sufficiently large number of such friends in orbit I could bear even the loss of several, I felt. This insurance policy added to the capacity for solo living I'd nurtured so assiduously in my time in the mountains and after, and the ever growing recognition there was no one and nothing I nor anyone else could in all sanity hang on to for security in our lives anyway, had come to leave me feeling reasonably 'free'. Would venturing to 'tie the knot' with you do anything to advance that freedom, or would it cause yet more ghastly entanglement? You see, Ruth, I wasn't sure.

I just sat and continued to admire your legs the far side of the table. I nearly got to blurting out the proposal after I'd had a couple, but each time I reached that point it was as if an angel came down from on high and stuffed my throat with a sock.

Once it was a very close run indeed.

It's my birthday, and we are *back* – hallelujah – in 'your' village as I always used to think of it where you'd been with Jim, the boys and then me. For a long time, you'll remember, you wouldn't set foot in it again after all that had befallen you, but as evidence of your freeing-up you could return now and enjoy the place afresh. Besides, Jim and Corinne had left. They'd retired to a remote corner of Scotland far away. It's as though you can have your old village back.

We're enjoying supper at the pub by the edge of the water, looking across to the hills. It's not the hot sunset-liveried evening we'd have liked – sitting outside with a glass at that spot remains for me one of the greatest delights of life even now – for it's *typical* June, unsettled, cold even, and we're cooped up inside. But hey, the sauvignon is a belter and it's a bit like old times, you and I down the Albion, would you believe, where once we had spent some of the happiest evenings and lunchtimes of our lives.

'We're a funny pair, aren't we?' you venture as you lean back with your goldfish bowl of wine, other hand fiddling with those untameable gipsy locks (rather, um, bottle-bright these days – I mean, *blonde*?)

'What d'you mean?' I hoot. I'm light. I'm also nervous. I suspect I know where this might be going. 'Funny? What's *funny* about us?' (One could argue we might more reliably be described as mad as hatters.)

'What's happened with us, I mean. The fact we're still here in this pub the two of us after all these years. All that's – happened . . . ' You fade away. 'Happened' feels a very English watercolour way of putting it. We would require a more robust canvas to do it justice, I believe. Something by Caravaggio maybe, or a Goya. No, Hierony-mus Bosch.

'It's a miracle we're not both down the loony bin. Permanently,' is my considered opinion.

You laugh. You're growing skittish. Christ, could that be 'coquettish'?

Where's the Emergency Exit?

'How many years is it now?' you flutter. Slurp.

'I've lost count.' You and I seem to go back to some prehistoric time divided by an ice age. You are most certainly thawing now. The hazel eyes blaze with hundred-watt bulbs. I'm thinking to myself, is there going to be sex rearing its head here, sort of a, gawd, 'birthday present' maybe? I do not know how I would handle that, at all. 'How are things with Desmond then?' I gabble, swinging the wheel hard right into detour.

'Fine. I'm a bit concerned, though. He's saying he's fallen in love with me and that, well . . . that makes it all a bit more difficult really. He'd never leave his wife, however; he's adamant about that. He'd never be able to live with himself he says, the condition she's in.'

'Where d'you stand? Yourself? Would you like to marry him?' Saved by the lovestruck Desmond.

'Oh no, I don't think so. He is lovely, though, have to say. What about *us*, though? I often wonder where you and I *are* these days, don't you?'

'Sorry?' I affect a sudden attack of deafness, or a brain tumour.

'Where you think you and I are *going*?'

'Same place as ever, I'd say. To hell in a handcart.'

'No, I'm curious,' you insist after kicking the drollery out of my left ankle with your right boot.

Here it is, isn't it, the perfect moment. *The* perfect.

'Well I was only thinking the other day, the same question. And I was reckoning we'd weathered a helluva lot and we're still afloat together, somehow, and . . . I don't know, I was just wondering how you might feel – just an idea to kick around at this stage, nothing definite, y'know, intentional, a proposal, anything like that – well, whether you might like to *consider* . . . ' And so forth between the clearings of the throat and a feverish licking of the lips as they turned into sheets of sandpaper.

But I didn't, did I? I bottled it.

'Oh I don't know, Ruth. No idea. I'm just pleased we've got to this point in one piece, basically, and we're the friends we are. In the end the very special ones I like to think we *have* managed to become. Don't you think?'

'Yes,' you said, very definitely. 'I do.' The pause thereafter admits no scrutiny, yet contains much thought. I give up chasing. I don't quite know whether it is relief or sadness visible now in *your* face, either. Had you wished for more? I shall never know now.

'You seem to be in quite an enviable place when you think about it,' I proposed. 'You've Desmond for the sex and me for the spirit. Oh, and Jim as your punchbag. Done 'n' dusted.'

Anyway I got home safely with my trousers on.

Let's not beat about the bush, Ruth. Sexually I was drying up, wasn't I? Perhaps 'that's it' now. End of my sex life altogether? Fiona was distinct backlist and there wasn't anyone else remotely on the horizon.

'We need to find you a *woman*!' you insisted with much concern, as if you yourself might have been an alien or something and not *the* woman who just happened to be the one I loved more than any on earth. 'We must get you some sex!'

You did, you frothed like a pimp.

'I'll settle for a cup of tea and a biscuit if that's alright,' I sighed.

'Aww c'mon, John, you mustn't give up. There's loads of life in you yet. Twenty more years at least!'

The prospect of twenty additional years of what I'd experienced sexually and emotionally in the past forty was enough to have me wishing fervently for euthanasia.

I puffed cheeks, ruffled my nose and I'm sure looked beaten all ends up. 'I'm tired, Ruth,' I said. It was the truth. No, I think I was coming to accept that sex wasn't worth the candle perhaps, whether in this orifice or that one. I had a good life beyond the bedroom, didn't I? A mounting reputation with my counselling, my friends, a home I loved and a vibrant inner life – love at all costs! – I honoured above all other. On top, very much in my life still, beating time to the music of the rest of it, delighting me as ever with her playfulness and caring, there was you.

Blues, demons, ECT, drugs, knives – all seemed such a long way off now. I marvelled at your rebirth; the young girl's spring in her step, the sexy swagger the older woman was capable of even now, the way she sometimes lifted her face to the light and smiled.

I, 'the intuitive one', did not know, did I? what was going on at all.

BY GOLLY, RUTH, YOU'RE MOTORING. Your life feels as though you're putting your foot down hard. Cancel this, and cancel that. Start up this group (the film circle 'Chickflicks'; great title) and get stuck into another (women's spirituality meetings). Social work, massage, running workshops, keep popping over to see Robin and girlfriend in Leeds, zap back and forth to join me when you can – phew! Excuse me while I get my breath back.

'What are you running from, Ruth?' I endeavour to ask one day.

'What d'you mean?' You sound breathy, almost excited.

'Well you . . . you just don't ever seem to *stop*, right? Always on the go these days, rushing pillar to post.'

'I'm busy, that's why. I've a lot on.'

'I appreciate that, Ruth, but I always thought you placed a lot of store on "being still" and "going slow". Seems it's going out the window, all that?'

You shrug. I've narked you – not for the first time, hey? I think you feel I'm trying to tell you how to live your life. Rightly, you feel I ought to sod off. Stop playing the teacher.

'I'm trying to think of ways of earning my living when I retire. The pension I'm going to get won't be enough to survive on. Nowhere near. Courses in parenting skills and building up my massage might be useful top-ups.' It all sounds eminently sensible. *OK.*

'Yeah, yeah, I'm sorry. I get a bit concerned for you, that's all. Don't want to see you getting ill again, do we?'

'I'm fine,' you determine, briskly.

'Good,' I sign off, lamely. I still hold on to what you'd said in your early weeks and months living alone in your new home, how you didn't always find that easy and you did, so often, look for ways to 'escape'.

Turn on the radio or TV, do some cleaning, phone someone to make sure you've somewhere to go tonight or at the weekend; you admitted you kept loneliness at bay like that, as of course do most people, afraid as they are to run into themselves in the no-hiding-place of solitude and silence. I just wondered whether what had happened to you in your breakdown, when everything in a sense did 'stop', was determining you never to 'stop' again. 'Stopping' was now more than teetering unease for you; could be it was experienced as out-and-out madness? And you didn't want to go back *there*, did you?

I saw less and less of you but that, after all, had always been part of the natural ebb and flow of our history. When we did meet up, you had plenty of bounce. You crackled. Plugging into Desmond, I jested, is lighting you up. You pull a buckled face. It was good sex, true, you reported. Again. That didn't ruffle feathers here; I *continued* to be glad for you, pleased you seemed increasingly fulfilled and happy. Maybe when all was said and done you weren't like me after all. You were not a natural solitary. You were more 'yourself' *with* people, in a relationship, and throve on the buzz that lots-of-things-to-do gave you. Everyone was different, weren't they? Compassion, Pepper . . .

I never stopped thinking about you, wondering where your life was heading; 'ours', too. I suspected the gallivant with Desmond wouldn't last forever and it was inevitable there'd be other men in your life. I thought, one day you're going to find a new partner, maybe a new husband, I bet. I used to look at that one head on and the thought jolted me even after all these years. I'd be happy for you, *would*, but I would also be sad. I still didn't want to 'lose you forever'.

At one point I raised this with you – the likelihood – and you picked at your nails, as you did, looked unsure for a while then flicked doubt away with a little shake of your head. You thought, 'A new relationship 'd be nice in theory but I can't see it happening. At my age there aren't that many available men around any more, you know.'

'Rubbish,' I said. If she wanted, Ruth France could have had hordes queuing at her door, I was convinced.

'There aren't,' you insisted. 'Not the kind of men I'd want to be with, let's say. And anyway I'm not sure I want to share my life with anyone again.'

'Ruth,' I reminded you, sternly, 'you were adamant about that one once before, weren't you, and promptly after that you'd a man living with you full-time. David. Remember?'

'Hah!' (You tried to make light of the bullseye.) 'I'm older 'n' wiser now.'

'Oh aye,' I doubted. 'Tell me about it.' I blew you a raspberry, a fond one, across the room.

'Well what about you then?' you retaliated. 'Look at the women in *your* life!' Put that in my pipe and smoke it.

'Yes but there's not a glimmer of anything other than straight-forward friendship with any of 'em. I don't have *designs* on a single one, I've told you.'

'That may be the case now but you wait and see in the future.'

'Since when were you any good at fortune-telling, France?'

You came back, as you used to do, with a new line altogether. 'I don't think I'm going to live to a ripe old age anyway.'

'Where've you dredged that one up from? I can just see you as a little ol' granny sitting in her rocking chair with grandchildren around you – and between now and then you've a whole new life ahead of you, starting *now!*'

You widen your eyes and look out into the swaying trees and the clouds invariably fluting dramatically over the hills beyond – *your* home's really special too, I reflect. 'I'd like that a lot but suspect it's not going to happen,' you said. 'I think I'll die fairly young.'

'You will if you carry on charging round the place like you are doing at the moment. But nah, not really, I think you're going to have a great old age. Sort of peace at last. I can see it. Honestly can.' And I did, hugely.

I got half of it right at least.

You weren't by this time looking forward to growing old. You mourned the thickening of your body, that puffing out of your face. Even in your forties you'd been slim. 'Now,' you reckoned, 'I'm losing it.'

'None of it matters,' I would insist, but because this letter to you is about being as truthful as I can, I couldn't deny the repining I experienced when I looked back on the old photographs. Fact is, France, you'd been a stunner. Today, though, your beauty is beyond all that; it is the person you've become. The merry old trouper you are.

'I'M EVER SO SORRY, can't make the lunch,' you give me good 'advance'. OK, I'm flexible. 'Forgive me,' the answerphone goes on another occasion, 'going to have to rule out Friday.' 'John, you're not going to believe this – oh lawd, I'm having to do it again – but . . . '

You're getting your knickers in a twist organising your diary. I shrug, as I do a lot these days. I leaf through one of your early letters and you're apologising, acknowledging the chaos, right from the start. And using the same to 'distance' yourself, even then.

'The time spent together has always proved to be special in one sense or another, but I don't hanker for any more – I honestly would drive you batty. My disorganised and erratic lifestyle is something that Jim found hard to cope with and he, like you, is disciplined and well-structured in day-to-day living.'

Weatherwise, it's turning out to be a disappointing summer. 'Bloody WINTER,' I growl, capital-lettered, in the diary under a sketch of storms. I'm in matching mood; uneasy, for some reason. I write: 'I feel at a "gathering" crossroads in my life. Nothing "holds" me other than that light. Where now, then?' I go down for a breather at a retreat centre, Othona, on the beach in Dorset I've been visiting for well over twenty years, and the inked clouds in the diary, designed like exploding bombs scattering shrapnel, continue. 'Cold, grey and horrible' the text. In an add-on, grubbied with self-pity, double entendre and contradiction – where the 'glad place' I'd been describing my life not long back? – I complain, 'I continually "miss out" on the sun!!' Yes, two clench-toothed exclamation marks, I'm afraid. 'Fed up,' I blather a few days later.

Back home, a young woman I'd met at Othona, 'Bridey', on a trek North, was my guest for the weekend and for the first time in what seemed like recorded time I invited a woman to bed. I knew as I was doing so I was behaving like a twit. I even knew what the answer would be: an unwavering *no*. Felt like end of an era, it did.

Then I went to see a film titled *Winged Migration*, which was the story of avian journeys around the globe. Soaring stuff. Yet the moment that touched me the most was one bird growing weary in flight and flopping into industrial slurry in a Russian rustbelt. It struggled to take wing again but, bit by bit, the filth slathered it till it could fight no more, sinking slowly to its death.

'Story of my life,' I grumbled at the bar afterwards, Cheerful Charlie that I'd become.

Gloom unconfined, finally I go cross-country to see (another)

Roger, friend of forty years whose sickbed I'd been coming to for the past five. Rog, a tiny withered homunculus, was dying. Seized-up with osteoarthritis, he'd given up the ghost. All day he just lay drinking and smoking, enraged. He was a little last scrap of heart-beat, curled like an old slipper, wrapped in a nappy. His dog Ben crapped and howled round the house. Roger tried to drown out pain and terror not only with the booze but with maximum volume on a news channel going round and round on a telly the size of a football field. Care teams came and went, feeding him slop. I would go outside a while to get some relief and gaze out blearily on broken-down factories and glowering valleys, and wipe shit off my shoes. Next door was overrun by a caged horde of dogs sounding like they wanted to rip throats out.

Once upon a time, in a fairytale, Rog had been best man at my wedding, my very best friend, a distinguished artist going on to become a college head of fine art. He used to be devastatingly handsome, a Viking with golden hair and beard, and women fell before him like harvested grain. Now he lies here, comprehensively embittered by life, a reeking 'corpse'. I still loved him, *too*, and told him. As everything fell away in our lives it was important, very, to do these things before it was too late.

Rog ended up a while afterwards as fertiliser for the wild flowers in his native Forest of Dean.

A few days after my trip to Halifax and its horrors, you and I meet again. You're in a pother. What's up? I wonder.

'I've something I need to tell you, John.' The 'need' is clear to see.

'What is it?' Summer has sprung at last and I've spent two days swimming outdoors. I'm feeling a bit better, I can tell, after these late weeks of niggle. But I realise that summer from now on is wrecked. You're picking the quicks on your fingers far too quickly, and I'm unsurprised you find it hard to look me in the face. Your own, I decided shortly after the event, was barefaced cheek. I don't like you like this whatsoever. It's a denial of all you stand for. *Are.* This is madness rampant still.

'I guess it's difficult for you,' I reflect, as though I'm bloody well counselling you.

'It is a bit.' You take a deep breath. 'You see, I'm seeing David again.'

I'VE BEEN WRITING to you through Christmas and New Year, eleven days non-stop. I've written, snacked, gone to bed, got up again and written. Beyond my window the days have been almost endlessly glorious, that slanting sunshine of midwinter shaping the world into cut glass, sunsets rainbow-coloured like its end, and the peace of a city from which it seems everyone has fled. I've not been miserable. Being here with you has been all that's mattered. I guess I've raised too many white wine Xmas toasts your way at the end of ten hours or more of writing. So, Happy New Year, y'ol' bugger.

God, you were one, no? What oh what was going on now? You were most definitely not a man-eater, prickteaser, nympho, arsehole or loony. But you were, Ruth dear, 'an old bugger'. A flibbertigibbet ('an impulsive, flighty person'), perhaps?

'*You see, I'm seeing David again.*'

Tell me about it. I wish someone would. At that precise moment of your announcing David's return, I hadn't a clue what was happening. Everything was a whirl. After what you'd just said, the world went silent. Stopped.

Who or whatever you are, 'flibbertigibbet' or something besides, the fact of the matter is you are beloved by *so* many, it is humbling to behold, as I sit here reading the tributes to you in the book of remembrance mourners lined up to write in after your coffin had been carted off to the flames. An 'old bugger' maybe, but such a sunny one lighting up so many lives.

Chris has mailed me copies of everything that'd been written about you at the wake, and the letters which have flowed in afterwards.

'Ruth, you were the most amazing person I ever met,' one individual writes. 'Whenever I messed up you were always there to pick me up and help me carry on. You supported me through everything even when you knew I was wrong. I will never forget you.'

'You felt like a fairy godmother to me, and your support lifted my heart,' writes another.

'I shall never forget your deep empathy, understanding, love and comfort after my breakdown,' a third. 'You are a very special person.'

You reached out and beyond without end.

'Thank you for your smiling eyes every time we met anywhere in town. They were filled with genuine love.'

'What a unique and wonderful fun friend you have been.'

'She was so thoughtful and cared so much and was willing to stand up for what she believed.'

'At a time when I and my family were in crisis and I was finding it so hard to get help, you came into our lives. You took your job as social worker so much to heart and were the only person who was committed and willing to give true support and practical help.'

Then, 'I learned the following from Ruth: "Everything that happens to you is your teacher. The secret is to learn to sit at the feet of your own life and be taught by it." I try to live this as she did.'

'I never heard anyone say anything bad about you ever.'

And there she was, 'seeing David again'. Hello Desmond, where in the picture right now are you? (Excuse me, Pepper – and *you*?)

BUT OF COURSE you weren't only a loving soul and an old bugger. The f-word, 'fun', crops up time and again in the record – you were source of so many laughs all over.

- 'You introduced us to gin. We couldn't stand for ages.'

- 'I will never forget the time you made me get out of bed because you wanted a hot chocolate and chocolate cake for breakfast, and we were nearly sick. Keep bouncing on them beds.'

- 'Your mum (Ruth) made Sarah a pizza in a square. And Sarah told your mum she didn't eat square pizzas, just round ones.'

- 'Christmas quote from Ruth: "Who cares about the goose? Let's have another glass of wine!"'

- 'I remember your warm heart and lovely nature, and the quails' eggs and champagne.'

And there were all the children who loved you, too.

'Ruth,' wrote one, 'I always felt she was as much a friend as a mate's mum.'

One Isobel, aged six, in her first joined-up handwriting: 'Dear Ruth, I can remember when we ran between the hills together.' Just that, signed with a kiss.

Reminders also of your many achievements, helping to dream and set up the county's first mediation service, for example, or starting the village's Christmas walk across the railway viaduct over the estuary 'back home', which was still a landmark tradition today.

Finally, the words of those closest to you. Your kid sister Tricia, whom you loved and at whom you raged so much: 'I remember the morning of my wedding day. She woke me with breakfast in bed, tea and toast, a single rose and earrings. It started my day in a special way. It is that attention to detail, to make people feel good, I will remember.'

Your husband Jim, talking about 24 November 1972, 'the first time we met', what you wore, your excitement at the prospect of working with the NSPCC, the National Society for the Prevention of Cruelty to Children, and the welcome your family extended to him: 'Above all I remember the days the boys were born, your pride and joy, and our lives changed forever.'

David (whose surname, Cole, I finally come by after all these years):

> 'Those ancient rocks have inscribed her name
> They will remember this one
> The weeping trees lament
> The sun shines and blesses
> Can we live as well
> Would we try this hard
> Can I?'

And so I've seen David for the first time since that initial encounter; he's pointed out to me across the room at the wake. I honour his love for you.

We don't meet, no. I doubt we ever shall.

There are first hints of the shadows in your life from cousin Barbara narrating fragments of your childhood: 'One day going to Old Bakery and finding Ruth had written in chalk "RUTH TIDY IS HARD DONE BY" on the walls and paths.' Hmm, oh yes – a foot-stamping tantrum *there* . . .

As for the 'fellers' in that glad and giddy life: 'When the new houses were being built next door, Ruth took a fancy to one of the young builders and would swing as high as she could (on the garden swing) to look over the fence to see him.'

Eeny, meeny, miny, mo – which one, eh?

My turn. I wrote that you were the most beautiful soul I had encountered on this earth, and the greatest love of my life. 'Each day of the rest of my life I shall remember thee,' I assured you, 'and endeavour to live that life with the love and wisdom you bequeathed to so many.'

I signed off: 'Godspeed your journey through the stars.'

BACK TO DAVID, to you standing there looking sheepish and silly. I can't be bothered interrogating you. I don't want to know whether you're in bed with him again and Desmond *too*. Enough. This time there's none of the old lurching inside, the hole opening up and my life falling down it, down and down. I feel calm. I begin to breathe normally again after the standstill. I don't make a scene, just peel away as soon as is convenient as though nothing has happened, and say 'See you.'

I drive home briskly. Door bolted, I don't reach for the bottle, or something to chuck. These things are of no importance what-soever. Our lives are but specks of dust among the stars. Nine galaxies for each human being on earth and each of those galaxies harbouring an average hundred billion suns, or so someone wrote somewhere – what point, our little pains?

I get into bed with a cold heart.

WE'RE SITTING in my car by the marsh. I've suggested we have a crack at doing something that's useful when people are at war, one person being allowed to speak without interruption for half an hour, just being listened to quietly by the other, then the other person being given their half hour in which to speak uninterrupted too. It can be a wonderful, wholly new experience for all concerned, the fact of the matter being that hardly ever do human beings listen to one another – they merely try to win the argument, as does the other geezer, and all that unfolds is the dialogue of the deaf. This is *the* core reason why there's so much unhappiness and bloodshed across the planet. We don't want to understand. We want to conquer. Listening is life's greatest skill, the royal highway to collaboration and kindness but, alas, is never taught at school, where competition and cunning are.

I have to confess, I wasn't listening to you that day; not properly. I can't remember a word you said. I wasn't interested in hearing what you had to say. You see, my heart had closed down. All that concerned me was that you got *my* message loud and clear. Lady, I'm 'out'. Now David's back, I don't want to know you.

So I sat for the requisite half hour 'listening' to you and, you told me at the close, I *hadn't* let you speak as agreed. I had interrupted. You were so angry with me.

Good to see it.

Now it was my half hour. I simply gave you your marching orders. I did so nicely. I didn't cuss you; indeed, I wished you and David the best. I'd got to the point in my life when wanting to 'do down' others had lost a lot of its appeal. The only person who got seriously hurt in such transactions was oneself.

I apologised for not keeping to my side of the bargain, and said I believed I'd butted in only to seek to clarify the odd point I was unclear about, not to question what you had to say. You said I'd interrupted you either to challenge what you were saying or dismiss it. I wasn't sure. We were arguing over the small print. You, though, weren't upset only at my alleged dialectical misdemeanour; you were seething at my axing you.

When we got back home I invited you in for a cuppa, a final brew. I was trying to lower the temperature, be kind. You weren't impressed. No, you didn't want to come in, thankyou. You said you had nothing more to say, then turned on your heel and marched down the road at a lick to your car. You roared off, belching flame. I shrugged and went inside.

You were still hopping some five months later, at Christmas. You sent me a card and a note, and the latter was steeped in nark.

I wasn't going to leave it there. In the New Year I wrote to you: 'At the end of the day I have only ever hoped that we might feel kindly about the other both during our time together and following the goodbye of last year, remembering with warmth and understanding what we've shared. I remain someone, Ruth, who'll always "be there" for you as a friend should there ever be need, your end, of such. That's how much you've meant to me through our travels, all the way from first meeting in September 1990. I'd like to hope we might remember the other with smiles?

'Ruth, you've told me so many times what's been "wrong" with me just as I've listened over a very long time to your finding fault with a fair stream of other "exes", family, friends, neighbours and work managers. Would you allow me to but bid you look, maybe, at the mote in thine own eye? I've had to confront my own shadow in its fullness, and integrate it, and finally come to use shadow as guide, for years and years in all my work and professional training. Yes, I've had no end of failings, I'm fully aware of them. And some, of course, remain. But I've also been deeply in touch with my integrity and worth and I shall, for my part, remember all those kindred qualities in you. I'll not forget the warmth of your heart, or the wicked light in your eye. I suspect we may never see each other again now. However, go well, friend, and flourish – I love you, as ever.'

After a little while you're able, Ruth, to write back:

'You will always have a unique place in my heart. I can't "not love" you. If you wish to make a formal goodbye I, of course, must respect that, but I still feel it to be inevitable that our paths will cross again and so will not be saying farewell at this point – just an "au revoir", I think.'

YOU'RE SPOT ON, aren't you? Two years pass. Another Christmas looms. Ruth France is once more in touch.

That's precisely where you've kicked David into – into touch. I'm again making little popping noises with my mouth. Dearest darling Ruth, what, on earth, are you up to now?

You look embarrassed, and I should think so too. In fact, you titter; naughty child. Am I pleased to see you? No, get ye gone. Baggage, Salome, I don't want to clap eyes on you again, ever. Spare me.

Of course I am pleased to see you. I'm chuffed. My sweet fireball Fiona has a go rolling her eyes now as well. I reckon she finds you and me incomprehensible. Off the radar. I think she's perceptive.

At one point it transpires you and David had even got to working, very briefly, as a professional team, running courses together in adult ed. He'd been back with his feet under the table *in your new home*. Same old story it would seem; he had nowhere else to go. You had, just before our last, two-hundredth, break-up, while you were regaling me with details of your and David's renaissance, invited *me* to the housewarming party at the flat that would be co-hosted by *him*. You must have been off your rocker, madam. Fiona was *right*.

'So David, we meet at last. Hello. What 're you doing with your-self these days?'

'Oh a bit of counselling here and there. Ducking 'n' diving, you know. And you?'

'Erm, much the same really. Lovely punch this, who made it?'

'Ruth.'

'It's amazing.'

'Yeah, 'tis.'

'What's in it, heavensake? It's got the kick of a mule.'

'Oh I dunno. One of Ruth's witches' brews most likely.'

'Wouldn't be surprised, no.'

'Dear ol' Ruth.'

'Dear ol' Ruth.'

'Cheers.'

'And to you.'

But then David had found another lady with pots of money and a big house, Skem way, and she'd fallen head over heels for him and wanted him to be her in-house, 24/7, spiritual teacher, with 'extras'. Too good an opportunity to pass on – and some. David had vamoosed with all his worldly goods in a spotted handkerchief on a stick over his shoulder. You are seething. I'm ever so pleased.

'He's a leech,' you rasp. 'An absolute con.'

'A cad,' I reflect, helpfully.

'I regret I ever got tangled up with him.' You look wonderfully flustered.

We're in a country house restaurant. The wine is tasting better by the minute. I make affirmative crosses between hums and gurgles totting up to early Christmas joy. I fashion myself a little Christmas present, a happy paper aeroplane, out of one of the napkins. My schadenfreude doesn't become me; one does *not* gloat over another's vilification or misfortune, Pepper. Even so, forgive me, I'm struggling not to take a night-off from my rectitude. 'Wheeee, hey-ho – *life,* eh Ruth?'

'I'm sick of it all and don't want anything more to do with him. Ever.'

'Till the next time then, hey Ruth!' I chortle. I have this sudden image of one of those Continental clocks, doors either side of the clockface, chiming on the hour with David emerging from one portal then going back in again, and me whirring out of the other and promptly vanishing too. Then up pops a bedroom scene out of a Whitehall farce, David and I alternating as the man in the wardrobe with his trousers off while the other bounces into the room, he in his underpants also.

'I mean it,' you insist, brushing aside my merriment.

'Ah well,' I burble, taking time-out from my counselling skills as well.

'I can't see how I didn't cotton on in all these years,' you mourn. 'My blindness, God I can't believe it! Must be something wrong with me.'

Pass.

You're still seeing Desmond, though. Yes.

Pass.

Christ it's Christmas, who cares? That's why we're here. You've rung to say it's the season of saying sorry for our sins, isn't it. *Our* 'season' ought to last a very long time, therefore. Right, then; eat, drink and be merry. You and I sparked into life on 15 December and now it's 16 December, sixteen years later. You warm my heart now as much as you ever did. More so. You and I, France – definitely 'cases'. We are.

IT'S A LITTLE OVER a month later, a horrible wet winter's evening at your place. We've eaten. We're glumped over the telly.

'D'you fancy a porn video?' you wonder, a voice no more animated than your proposing, say, a Malteser.

I shrug. 'You've still got some then, have you?' I ponder, surprised. (Am I?)

'Three or four,' you respond, nonchalant as possible. Not a *barrowload*, you'd like me to know. I think the deliberately dirtiest movie I'd seen up to this point in my life had been *Confessions of a Window Cleaner* in, well . . . Barrow. It was a night-out from my hermitage in the hills – spiritual rapture needing a night-off too – and the film was excruciating.

'Do you,' I flutter, 'want to watch one?'

'Why not? What d'you fancy?'

'What've you got?'

You shuffled the pack. 'There's a threesome, one stud up the woman's front end and the other at the back, and "hot lesbian action". And, erm . . . ' You have to get your specs out for the next one.

'Any. Don't mind,' I say, waving my goblet around the room.

So we start with the ménage à trois. I'm aghast. I had never before seen such enormous cocks. Genuine fixtures they were. Black man, white man, it's all the same. My lunchbox, by contrast, is a chipolata and a couple of cherry tomatoes. Discombobulating. Surely they can't 'do it'? They'll kill her.

The lady, however, takes in one then the other as though she might be entertaining the vicar. I-do-not-believe-it. She's not in agony at all; she's joy all over. The two penises must be whopping together inside her like Punch and Judy. The three of them are standing up, the men snogging her then themselves, hands round each other's arses with the lady an animated sandwich-filling between. When the three of them climax together, if such they do, they make enough noise to wake the dead. What the storyline was I no longer have the faintest idea.

Yet I have to acknowledge there's a smidgen of steam in the gusset at home.

Even more rumbustious, however, is the lesbian epic. This gets gynaecological in close-up, legs so far apart they might be inhabiting different galaxies. Hands bang in and out of fannies as though drilling for coal. Tongues and teeth slather and gnash. Oh, and thank you for the anus allegedly jiggling for joy on a dildo the diameter of a fire hose. The two women are coated in oil so thick they slither over one another like seals on crack. The script is pretty basic; a concatenation of squeaks, squeals and Alfred Hitchcock screams. I hope Doug next door hasn't got his deaf-aid in.

It's been some performance. There's more to come. We're a bit drunk and horny. You take me gently into your bedroom and lay me out as though you might be unrolling a map. You make love to me so very differently from anything just seen. You nip, and nibble, like a rabbit; kiss me with such softness that tears arise and I reach round to hold you tightly, that you might never leave me, go, again.

I can't believe this is happening after all this time. It's as if the years of strife have never been and we're the Young Ones once more. My mind flits with questions imponderable. Why have we been apart this long? What's 'stopped' us? Can and will we 'get there', even now?

The dark rain slashes at the window, the wind moans around the hills outside, and I curl up into you as though you have always been my refuge and ever shall be. The tears are falling. You stroke my hair with one hand and, reversal of our *Brief Encounter* start, quietly take the tears away with the fingers of the other.

Yet I'm too afraid by now to say, 'I love you.'

We don't spend the rest of the night together. In the spare bedroom there's nothing left but the dark and *so many* questions flying around like flocks of startled birds. Your tenderness, the way you reach straight into me, touch my heart as ever you did.

And then I sleep. I dream my old dream. I'm high above the city on a tightrope slung between two white towers. I'm walking the wire. It's swaying in the wind, and I'm frightened. Part of me longs to go back to the safety of where I've come from, but a greater self refuses to allow me, and drives me forward – *on*! I don't even know what I'm 'driving forward' to, only that I have to proceed in this one clear direction. I curse the fact I climbed this high in the first place and dearly wish I'd stayed in the warm scrumble of the city below, but even now I know that down there lies only slow death; madness. I must press on, dancing the wire between sunshine and storms.

Porn to drunken fuck to fleeting glimpses of love; swirling between sleep and waking, there is no stopping the dancing.

The next day there's a blank in my diary. Not a word.

THERE WASN'T A WORD either, afterwards, between the pair of us about 'that night'. I never quizzed you, nor you me. 'So what exactly went on *there* then?' You must have been as confused as I was.

So why did we stay mum I wonder? For my part, I feel it was a mix of things. There was bit of me ashamed, almost, at having lowered myself to porn while at the same time being aroused by it. Wasn't the kind of thing I'd 'do normally', was it? It was alien. Not that I was a prude about these things. I was all for erotica evoked with artistry and flair. This had been junk. Yet, remind yourself Pepper, it *had* got your juices going and pornography never sought a billing more fancy than that. Next, I think I had a fear pretty deep-rooted by this time that I could go on and on wanting you yet never get anywhere with you, David the Divine in frame or no, so it was going to be better for my health in the future if I kept you at a good arm's length *forever*. Third, I loved you still, didn't I? But was I physically attracted to you any longer, assaying the matter without porn and booze in the picture, and thinking straight, that is? Was I *really*? I had to confess: I had some doubts. Would I, therefore, ever again want us to come together as *partners*? See, I wasn't sure.

It was better to say nothing about these things that left one scratching one's head, no, and wait patiently in the wings till some clarity dawned?

Thus the year gets under way with the two of us gadding all over the place again as friends. There's a noticeably increased sense of space between us, not so much in the sense of either of us distancing themselves from the other in self-protection – though for me there was an element of that as I've indicated – but more in recognition that the greatest gift one human being can give another, after love, is space. It comes naturally with love's territory anyway. And what I mean by 'space' is the removing from one's relationships of all those things that otherwise erode and eventually wreck them; moulding the other person to your desires, playing games with them, trying to aggrandise oneself in some way at the other's expense, fearing they do something that may harm you and, in a thousand and one ways, endeavouring to get them to scratch your itches and tick your boxes. It was the 'space' that said, 'Hey, do, say, go, have what you want. D'you mind if I join you sometimes for the ride? For the fun.'

Because I didn't remotely need you any longer I no longer needed to capture you. I had long ago in my life seen love as a gorgeous butterfly we all of us chased with our nets. When we caught it we put it in a jar, and killed it. I wouldn't chase after anyone or anything ever again. Instead, I'd learn to be still so that a butterfly might alight on me of its own accord.

Right then, France, 'back together' (whatever that may continue to mean in our case), shall we knees-up? We do. Went on holiday for the first time since our weeks in Ithaca, way back. Another life, another age, another island – we were captivated by the things – and this time it's Crete. We hole up in an old taverna on the beach. That's all there is, an inn. No development, village, hamlet – *nothing*, is there? That magic word again.

When we dropped down through the mountains to spy our hideaway for the first time from afar, we could scarcely believe our eyes, could we? It was, as it cheerfully described itself, 'completely on its own'. Way back it had been a warehouse for the storing of carob nuts brought across the sea from Africa. It had four blue and white bedrooms and a terrace restaurant, and that was it. There was, joy, 'nothing to do' there except gaze out to sea, swim, read, meditate, eat, guzzle the extremely potable farmers' wine, and enjoy the cicada chorus at night. There being no light anywhere around us, the stars were close enough to talk to. My favourite solo activity was swimming way out to sea so I'd have no one near and there lie on my back for aeons, fingers cupped like little flowers, mind empty of the dross of all our lives and in touch, instead, with the gold at their centres.

You gave the water a wide berth, naturally. There were too many shadows and holes in the swells around the rocks and the sounds for you, even with the sunshine and wine, of poet Arnold's 'melancholy, long, withdrawing roar' down the 'vast edges drear' of the ocean. I think you went in a couple of times on the baby strip of pebbles the other side of the terrace wall. You lay down and splashed. Splish splash, and you're out.

'That's fine. No I don't want to stay in any longer. That was just right,' you insist when I attempt to pick you up and fling you out to sea (I'm joking). 'I'm very happy for you to swim over to Libya if that's what *you* want. I'll have a nice cold beer standing by for when you get back.'

There are little wild cats in the jungle of prickles at the rear and within the first couple of days they're eating out of your hand. Literally. The management would prefer to shoot the bloody things but you are distressed by their decrepitude and mewlings and spend much of the day gathering gobbets of food with which to feed them when they drop down in the evening after the heat of the day. You sit with them on your knee or snuggled up to your breast. Bleeding, manky, smelling of things indescribable; it matters not. Ruth has magically arrived out of the heavens to minister unto them. The beasts get a bit confused however, one moment having rocks hurled at them by the staff, the next, manna gently proffered by you. They lie in your arms with eyes of adoration shining through infection and fleas.

I know, there's a little bit of jealousy in the reckoning here isn't there? It used to be the same didn't it at Woodlands? Someone phoned up out of the blue or called round with a crisis, great or small, and no matter what *we* might happen to be doing off you would go on your rescue mission. You couldn't help yourself in this almost promiscuous helping of others. I do have not a few memories, clenching my teeth and snorting frustration. *Mother Bloody Teresa of the Mountains*: hey, what about *me*?

You should be on song. Your life is perking up. You'd retired at last from social services after being head-hunted by Barnado's, your reputation championing the causes of damaged children preceding you. The new post was part-time, so ahead lay more freedom than ever. I was proud of you. You'd put in over forty years now, working for disadvantaged kids. It had been an honourable record. Best of all, you'd been *excited* by the new work ahead and the many challenges this too would bring. Going to Crete was by way of a celebration.

There was a small cloud in the sky wasn't there, though. Yes, you'd rid yourself of your collywobbles in the old job but now discovered you were saddled with a boss you claimed was all head and no heart. Barnado's itself did things a lot differently from your own historic way of working. It was more bureaucratic, tick-box, computer-driven and dull. You'd started taking deep breaths; c'mon Ruth, you were telling yourself, it'd be like this at the start of any new job. Be patient, give yourself time to bed in, slowly work the old experience into pastures new. I told you, 'I know you can do it, Ruth. You've so much to offer, you'll make a go of it no matter how the new systems work. Go easy on yourself. And remember it's only two-and-a-half days a week now, not five. Hey Ruth,' I'd half high-fived you, '*bliss!*'

Yes, you'd said, I was right.

Meanwhile here's to this New Life; and we'd toasted just that as we sat in our first Cretan sunset unable to believe our luck at having found this glorious secret place.

There's a fierce north wind, the *meltemi*, blowing the sea into a frenzy of little waterspouts in silver and pink, the 'castaway' palm fronds roofing the terrace rattle and sing. The air feels like velour and you seem happy, at rest, beside me. We're maybe cracking it, France, at last. It is as though we're back on Ithaca; cats for rats, say. And more settled, by miles.

As the days go by I write in the diary: 'This Is a Zen holiday. Free, without fear, and simply flowing "with" time.'

Halfway through our stay I observe of the two of us: 'Not the glimmer of unrest.'

What's happening to my 'intuition'? I was again a bit slow, then, to pick up on things wasn't I? *I* saw no cloud, even though at times I did feel a slight and passing chill breeze all my own. You retreated quite a lot to your bed, 'to rest'. Sometimes I'd watch you across the way and there might be a small perplexity in your gaze. Occasionally you seemed far away but it was brooding, not meditation. I put it down to time-of-the-month, something you'd eaten or 'too much wine', perhaps, the night before. None of it meant much. Usually you were upbeat and full of Crete.

In hindsight, as ever, things start to add up. There's a photograph of you on your balcony, leaning on the wall as you look far out to sea. Your arm is lifted to your face and a finger lies reflectively across your lips. I look hard, moving the print backwards and forwards, and it's possible to discern that you might be about to cry.

But I scribble in my notes: 'Still a lovely quiet with Ruth, and a little wondering (now) what might have been. I think we've been very happy together, but, CHECK,' I order myself. 'I do, and the answer is *very* positive.' That was true, I see now. 'Together' we're fine. The problem, this time, is when we aren't. Some turnaround.

I think what diverted me, especially, from what was going on in your life at this time was your very evident joy at the arrival of your first grandchild. Rob and his beautiful, soft-spirited Rachel had given you baby Anya. She was a barrel of fun and you and she had bonded like Bostik from the off. You had the child to look forward to when you got back.

But even little Anya isn't enough to spare you now. Holiday over, you return to the hills and the 'little cloud', out of my eyeline, is starting to mutate into thunderheads.

You're 'not right'. You go ill from work, ending up staying a while with Rob, then again with Chris. You already know the truth but keep it hidden from what would be a startled world: you're not going back to Barnado's, you've decided. You'd given it a final go but there'd still been no fulfilment at day's end, ever. It was over; all of it.

Rob and Rachel are planning to move away from the North of England, maybe go abroad even. There was the prospect you wouldn't see very much of Anya in the future after all. Your last anchor would be gone. Your other, your job, was in reality hoisted already.

Perhaps there was one last hope. Desmond? No. He too you now let go of. You'd tired of being a mistress. The long journeys the two of you had to make to get away from the area where Desmond lived with his deteriorating wife, as he didn't want anyone to see him with you and start tattling; the times he'd had to scuttle away from you in public when he nevertheless spied someone he did know; the whole round of Desmond's trying to preserve his reputation as a 'devotedly loyal husband' in a life with you of subterfuge and tension – everything else unravelling around you, even so you'd had the courage to end it. 'I can't go on living like that,' you'd said, 'if the whole purpose of my life now is to become more *real*.' Desmond had been heartbroken. He did love you in his own convoluted way. You'd been sad. But that was the end; there was no going back. And, regrettably, Desmond couldn't take a deep breath and come and say goodbye at your funeral when it came.

Finally, it had happened: you'd run right out of identities and purpose. Suddenly (you'd been here before) there didn't seem a lot left for you between now and death. Your spirituality felt, in your worst moments, to be self-deception. Sham. Morning to night your days, if you weren't careful, were in danger of turning into deserts.

You were no different; you did what countless others do when they discover there are not a lot of 'things to do' in their lives any longer, that their days amount to nothing very much. Only, on this occasion, with you it wasn't the 'nothing' you and I had once learned to praise and hearken to, the hard-won *plenum void* full of unimaginable potential, leaving us free of the chains of our pasts. This was a 'nothing' filled only with darkness and dread. 'Just what is the *point*?' Terrifying, that one. You tried to run away from the terror rather than turning and engaging with it, face to face. Back to the old ways, Ruth. This time you eschew pills and volts, and drink yourself *silly* instead.

Here was when you started to 'drown' in the deep, dark water of your sorrows. There were fathoms in you unexplored, where no light had got to yet. When you shut your eyes, you would one day tell me, you used to experience yourself drowning right there. So sleep went; you would lie awake for nights and weeks on end, afraid to close your eyes and rest. This only made you spiral, sink the more. Down and down and down you went. You poured poison down your throat and gasped and choked for breath, then drank more to stop the choking. And when you spewed your insides across your blankets or floors you drank more heavily still to blank that out too. You didn't want to be conscious, eyes open or shut, any longer; just that. Oblivion, *please*.

Beyond intention, awareness even, you were drinking yourself to death.

All I heard from you, Ruth, was: 'I'm ill.'

Time after time you cancelled arrangements. When I did see you once in a blue moon you were a reeking, puffed-up grotesque. Your breath alone made me turn away in disbelief; it stank of sewers. We go see a movie – perfect. Title: *Crash*. This is what your life has turned into, one long slow-motion *crash*.

And being a drunk you do what drunks do: you lie. To your children, friends, to me: you lie. You say one thing, do another. And all this from the woman who has declaimed to so many now: 'I need to be honest.' In reality you're all shuffle and mumble, evasion and shit.

No, I very definitely don't like you like this, or want to have sex with you, or remotely hope to consider you as my 'partner' once more. You're becoming fat and ugly and two-faced. *Sor–ry.*

But I do love you, and I shall never turn away from you. I'll soak up your tears and wipe away the sick; I'll always be 'here' for you, I promise, no matter what.

The year, 2007, sags towards its close. In December all five of our scheduled get-togethers fail to materialise. At Christmas there's nothing, and I can't make contact with you on the phone. You're firmly under the care of the boys and their partners, shut off from the rest of us. At least, after all you have imbibed these past months, it's good you're alive still. It is bloody amazing.

Note – beloved Ruth, have faith – I've an ace up my sleeve.

I TAKE YOU TO SEE AKONG. It's just after Christmas and I've written to ask if he might see you and give you some healing, 'save your skin'.

You're anxious. 'I don't know what I'm going to say to him,' you cavil.

'You don't have to say anything. I told you, I've explained everything in my letter. He's bang up to date with what's what.'

The lama knows you've become a drunk, that there are times now you'd rather die. Your life is crap. Akong, I know, would venture to suggest that all of that was rather auspicious. *Sooooo* much to celebrate there; all that rubbish just waiting to be turned into riches. You watch. Trust me, France.

The Venerable Akong Tulku Rinpoche, born in 1940, is one of the world's great healers. When the Chinese invaded Tibet in the fifties, Akong fled over the Himalayas on foot. To survive in the snows he even had to eat his shoe leather. To this day he is revered throughout Tibet as a saint. He was abbot of a famous monastery there and then founded a monastery in Scotland instead. One of a trio of distinguished Tibetan teachers who escaped from their country at the same time, they were the first lamas ever to come to the West. They became known as The Three Wise Men. Akong is not only a Buddhist master, he's a doctor of Tibetan medicine too. And a professor. Further, he heads a charity, Rokpa, an operation with an annual three-million-dollar franchise in stricken countries such as Tibet, Nepal, Zimbabwe and South Africa, and more than a dozen other, serving food to the homeless, running schools, children's homes, farms, craft centres, hospitals and scores of other projects set up to benefit individuals and communities shafted by life. He's a friend of the Dalai Lama and goes to Bejing to treat with the Chinese authorities, regularly. Even they think rather a lot of him, one government citation in '08 describing him as 'a star who shines with great compassion'. The Chinese are allowing him to organise rebuilding of some of the monasteries ravaged during the Cultural Revolution. Oh and he's married, to an Englishwoman now called Yangchen, and has a family.

His teaching – he has thousands of students one corner of the earth to the next, though doesn't see them as 'students', only 'friends' – is unorthodox to say the least. As a 'friend' of his who used to go and see him with a clipboardful of questions, ex-journalist and chaser of mysteries that I was, I once found myself ordered by him to put the thing away and 'go and get out of your head and into your body instead.' How? By running nine-and-a-half miles to a village downvalley, then promptly turning round and running the nine-and-a-half miles back. I did. Nineteen miles. It was night by the time I returned, feet a mess. I had to see Akong again before turning in. He said he was pleased with my commitment to the teaching and told me to set off next morning and run to Lockerbie, an even greater distance. Gasping, I pointed to the bloodied, elastoplastered pulp that went by the name of my feet, but Akong just smiled (he was always smiling, even with global collapse on the way) and said, 'Never mind, I'd still like you to go.'

So next day I set off, weaving down the road like Ruth France after a few, and reckoned by the time I got to Lockerbie I'd just about be dead. After five-and-a-half miles I can't go on – I'm finished. I turn round. The five-and-a-half miles back, I'm never going to be able to make 'em. I'm on a bleak and lonely road in forest; middle of winter, hardly a car to be seen. Ah here's one coming this way, finally, thank Christ. I stick out my thumb for a lift. And as the vehicle draws level then simply pooters on past, I cannot believe what I've just witnessed. It was Akong Rinpoche in the passenger seat, giving me a smile a bit knowing and frosty, and waving like the Queen.

Unusual practices, as I say. But he's the person who has done more for me and my life than any other. There was that time I didn't want to go on any more either, remember?

Samyê-Ling (meaning 'a place beyond imagination or concept') is the largest Tibetan monastery in the world outside Tibet. It's a Cecil B. De Mille movie set dropped into ghoulish dark conifer forest and bleak hills otherwise sensibly avoided in the main by human life. The temple is so brightly coloured I tell new visitors I'd recommend shades. Monks and nuns in maroon and saffron robes, beetling hither and thither in their solitudes and dreamy smiles, or sometimes their transparent neuroses, look like visitors from other times and worlds, which in a sense they are. A friend of mine arriving at the place for the first time said the over-riding question it left him with was: 'What do these people know that I don't?' I suspect the lama himself might have answered: 'Nothing.' Adding perhaps, if pressed, 'All the answers you seek are within you and available now.' If that left you scratching your head, wanting to know, 'OK, so how do I go about making those answers available?' I wouldn't have been surprised had the lama then said, 'Stop searching.'

Your mind in a total tangle, the problem in the first place – work that one out. *Let go*, instead?

So you go and meet the lama, no idea what to expect, and when you emerge from his embroidered sanctuary after ten minutes you haven't a clue what's gone on, have you? You just look baffled.

'All I did was tell him briefly what you'd said in your letter and how awful I'd been feeling and . . . ' You trailed off and shrugged. 'Basically that was it.'

No flashing lights or rainbows or anything like that, were there? Just a little man with mangled English, telling you what?

'Nothing really.'

'And after nothing, what then?' I revert to being the telly interviewer.

'I'm not sure. It's all a jumble. He just said he'd pray for me when I asked if it'd be alright if he gave me some healing.' You're resolutely unimpressed.

I smile. I've been here before, so many times. You and he merely sat in silence for a few moments, and that was it. Job done. *Healing through presence alone.*

Your life was never the same thereafter, was it? Talk about 'all change'! As one of your friends wrote in the book of remembrance after your death: 'Dear Ruth, I feel your soul strangely at peace and am so pleased your last few months were so happy and free. Just what you deserve.'

I'm excited by what's happening to you. I have no idea where this is going to end now but do know the outcome will in some way be blessed. I see Rob and he nods, says, 'There's a big difference, isn't there?'

Ruth, do you know this? Probably not – but you are growing beautiful again by the day.

In your heart, at last, you were becoming the dancing queen in the shocking red dress. A free spirit, *that most desirable of beings.* You couldn't give a stuff any longer about owning anything, planning the future or worrying-about-everyone. You could be on your own and have a day doing nothing, and that no longer drove you to doing-or-drink.

Robin and Rachel get married in Leeds town hall, and baby Anya and you go off for days at a time, you loving every moment of the tiny child's curiosity and laughter, the long hours you wander together, buddies, bums, around the streets, parks, caffs and galleries of the resurrected city. You know it's probably only going to be a short time together. But you are living entirely in the 'now'.

You come back to me newly born. It is as dramatic as that. Remember that time we were talking and I said, 'This is the beginning of your *real* life, Ruth, at last.'

You agreed.

I watch you with such tenderness and joy. This is the best time of my life too. The clouds have gone. I'm growing older yet younger by the moment, sailing towards my end like a little paper boat lit by a candle, out towards the sea. I've no fear that way. My will and last wishes are 'done' and you and friend Annette I take to dinner as my (newly appointed) executors after I'm gone; another birth-day, and a 'thankyou' both. As the glasses clink I joke: 'I reckon I'll outlive the pair of you nonetheless.' And how did you, equally light-hearted, respond?

'I'm sure you will!'

WE'RE WALKING, you and I, along a river exiting one of the far northern lakes at t'other end of the mountains, a saunter, seven or eight miles. It's a beautiful June day, a breeze cutting up the water into impressionist lights. A couple of fishermen are parked up at one point but, otherwise, there's no other human traffic. An occasional trout skewers up and out of the water, then back. The little riverside trees rustle like foil. I'm falling into a sunlit trance. There's not a lot to talk about because there's no need. You're away in your own world too. It's companionable heaven.

By the time there's tarmac again, I'm way in front. I sit on a wall and watch you materialise from a distance. And here you are, that rolling gait as sexy as ever, your right arm flicking at the wayside with a stick, sucking in the sights and sounds around you like a Hoover. It's at that moment sitting there, tea and an Alan Bennett play at the lakeside theatre ahead, trance real as the fritillaries and martins, that I admit to myself – I know, can't help it. O glory – I am, very definitely, falling in love with you all over again. Not that I'd stopped loving you, ever; it was but a marked deepening of the love I bore you already. A kind of spectacular gear change, say. You and I, I know, are *one*.

All of it the beginning of what was to be a spectacular end.

THE VALE, Jackie's valley, becomes our summer home. 'Twelve weeks of warm bliss,' I hope in the diary, looking ahead to the rest of the season in England then the time set to follow in Greece. In Jackie's ancient stone pile on the fellside we are Lord and Lady of the Manor. Time seems to melt. We take treats to the long-haired goats and ridiculously tiny ponies that come charging over the fields like cavalry the moment they spy us on the horizon with our paper bags. Mother of all fights then as the beasts butt and rugby-charge a way to the front for a feast. The stately horses I love to sit with and talk to as the day unfolds from misty grey dawns. And they do; the creatures answer. The cats enjoy my lap and Sara, pretending to be fierce, snarling like a bad actor, would like to chase balls and sticks forever. You?

I hold you close when we come together, more tightly than ever, as though there's part of me in the shadows that knows something's up. Our happiness feels so intense. Too good to last, could be?

'So,' I venture, 'where are you now then?' As the days go by I am watching your breath slow down, your body unfolding like a flower in the sunshine, *the hand with the knife* peeling an apple more steadily than I can remember; the way you curl up by the fire at night now with not a lot left to say or do. I think you're coming close to content.

'I think,' you say, 'the running has stopped. I can't remember feeling like this. Ever.'

'It's lovely to see, Ruth. But gawd, talk about peace hard-won . . .' I reach across the table (we're having lunch) and waggle your forearm affectionately.

'True,' you muse. 'But I don't regret any of it. Been tremendous learning. It has, right the way through.' You don't by this point carry the smallest regret in your life, do you? Sadness, pain, a few questions, some uncertainty about things; yes, such remain. But you're forged by fire. I have never known you with bitterness in your heart; a smidgen, ever. I know I can't say the same. 'I think,' you conclude, 'I am very lucky.'

That night, before we retire, separate rooms as ever, I hug you and in the snuggle kiss your head, as I had that day, long ago, on the marsh. It's our first 'kiss' since the impromptu spooning spiked with porn and booze. I try to disguise the act here as an accident almost, an inconsequential brushing of the lips along the greying hair; fond echo as it were of times past, and passion. You're holding me differently, I can tell. Till now, through these long years of our separated state, when we have met we've reached out to the other with arms a little stiff and wary sometimes, even clockwork? True? But now – yes, that is the right word – we're starting to *snuggle*. Just a bit, and shyly. I realise I am not afraid of you any longer. I think I'm free at last to love.

Another evening we're talking about the healing you've had. 'Everything,' you're convinced, 'started to change with the meeting with Akong. It's been a different world since.'

And what in your own words does it feel like then 'to be healed'?

'It's like not having to ask more questions,' you reflect, exploratively (Akong would thoroughly approve of that one, France). 'That everything in my life is alright as it is and meant to be this way. There aren't any niggles left, no. *That's right*.' You got there. Adding, hauntingly in retrospect, 'If I died tomorrow it'd be perfectly OK. I'd have nothing to fret about; you know, things left undone or dreams unfulfilled. I feel *held* by the universe now. Loved by it at last.'

'But Ruth the boys have loved you for thirty years and hundreds of other people have felt exactly the same way about you all through your life.'

'I know that,' you hasten. 'Put it down to my being a slow learner, but you see it's knowing I'm not just loved by *people*; I am by life itself. Whatever happens to me now I feel, on some inexplicably deep level, I'm *safe*. The universe 'll look after me from now on. Totally. The release, the relief, from that one, it's immense. Knowing this changes everything in an instant. I can go to bed now and sleep in peace.'

As I look back I see you were writing the script for your end, as though 'on some inexplicably deep level' you knew it was coming. Soon.

SUMMER ITSELF, now it's *struggling*. 'The nuclear winter continues,' I grump in the diary. The valley is being lashed week in, week out, with endless, bitter rain.

But the day Rob, Rachel and the child come to say their good-byes – they're off to their new lives in Kenya any day – the monsoon breaks, the sun appears, and among the battered bees, darting swallows and shaggy windblown blooms we picnic in the old garden, all five (six, with Sara). A photograph shows you with baby Anya in your arms. You look serene. It's a final reminder of all that you'd dedicated your life to, the love and care of the defenceless child. It's forty-five years since you pushed your first pram then went off to London to train with the NSPCC, but 'the project' will never end for you, I know.

There are tears all round as we embrace at the last; your impending loss, it's plain, is huge. You might see Rob only once or twice a year at most now, and all your dreams of being 'grandma down the road' are gone. I'm upset because I'm, in a sense, 'losing a son'.

Robin, Rachel and Anya drive off, waving. It's the last they'll ever see of you.

Shortly after, you leave for St Andrews university, Saint Salvator's chapel, to attend the wedding of Chris and Lura while I get on with my life in the city. There's a picture of you in pink, sprightly fascinator in your hair, laughing hugely with Lura and Chris's best man, Stuart Bak, and even from here your roar is infectious. There are other photographs: you've lost weight, the clingy dress drapes your body voluptuously; you look dazzling. I realise I still fancy you, hugely, after all. I'm a bit amazed at myself. I could muster a very serious *growl* over some of these glamorous shots of you, France.

Come back to the valley soon, sister!

And the time arrives. Chris and Lura kiss and wave you off. You're 'smiley, happy and clearly enjoyed the wedding,' Chris says.

It's the last they'll ever see of you as well.

WE FLY INTO MANCHESTER from that idyll in the islands. It's raining, a deluge, and we get soaked to the skin waiting for a taxi at a stand with no cover in the wettest metropolis in England. Welcome home.

Beyond the awareness of either of us, things are unravelling fast. On our adventure, wonderful though it had been, you'd lost a phone, camera, bag and a thousand euros in four separate incidents during the month. It was almost as if you were throwing everything away now; as you'd said, you weren't interested any longer in 'things'. Inevitably, it had all caused a few more eyeballs this end, as it would.

Even so, it is catching. At the airport hotel I lose my electronic room key. When I get home I find I've lost my passport. It turns up weeks later, after you're dead, under the bed in your room at Jackie's. I'd never set foot in the place. You've picked the passport up and pocketed it, obviously. Then chucked it.

Please, universe, what are you up to?

Our last evening is spent by the fire. Whiffs again of my wanting; wouldn't it be good if you and I could live like this, in a place like this, for good now? Just the two of us, growing old together in days evaporating ever more into light and silence? All we'd 'done' *that* day was sidle along another river and have coffee and cakes. This evening I've brought more logs in, opened another bottle and chopped the vegetables for supper. It is all of it enchantingly simple, a whole load of fun. 'Wash a bowl,' bids a Zen injunction, 'and wash your mind.' Enlightenment, anyone? 'Hew wood, draw water,' goes another instruction. Do it with focus. Do it with love. *Everything*. (And as for 'loving' the likes of Hitler, or your mother-in-law, or whomever – well, rank opposition, dogged patience and unfailing courtesy might all be perfectly fine embodiments, surely, of the impulse to *care*?)

I'd been thinking about that Big Question – 'What Next, Ruth?' – over the last few days. I would sit and watch you in the firelight, reading, thinking to myself, 'Go on, suck it and see.' Told myself to 'stop the mind games' (Akong's voice in the background). 'In your heart,' I urged myself on, 'look at her – what d'you *feel*?'

'Much love.'

'That case, what's the problem?'

'Me.'

No, I kept putting it off. There was plenty of time. I'd be returning to the farm at the weekend; this isn't my last night *really*.

I put it all away and did the crossword instead. Fear 1, Love 0.

GOD, THE RAIN. It's started pouring again and it goes on and on. But it's warm and cosy by the fire here with Sara and the tigers, the wine, my scribbled notebook of thoughts and phrases, this week's *Guardian* review; then thinking about my eight clients scheduled for tomorrow and the rest of the week, most of whose lives are changing for the better; plus the choral 'do' I'm singing in at the weekend, basso profundo, down in my boots. It is, *my* whole life's on song, so.

Am I kidding myself? This 'love', just a drug? No mention of it so far in the decoding of the seven hundred and fifty thousand typed (single line) A4 pages of the human genome. 'All hope, all passions of any sort,' the lab technicians tell us, are but 'illusions which go to serve the purposes of the genes.' As for what those 'purposes' might be, ultimately, well, 'Evolution is not going anywhere. It doesn't want anything and it doesn't give a toss,' writes one Midas Dekkers in *The Way of All Flesh: A Celebration of Decay*. Are we all no more than scientist William Hamilton's 'essentially tragic figures, divided against ourselves, pretending to a unity that, deep inside myself, I now know does not exist'? This love letter to you, what's it all about *really*?

'Fancy a cocoa with some rum in it?' you pipe up out of nowhere across the last flames of that last day's end.

Course I do. Bring it on. I'm camped there with one fat cat on my chest and the other splayed belly up and legs akimbo like a tart across the cushions at my side, Sara snoozing, one eye open, in her bed, the wind singing under the eaves, rum and love in my heart, you across the way, lit with fire, *at peace at last* – and could there ever have been a happier evening with which to close our time together if you'd tried?

ONE SERPENTINE BEND to the next, on foot, I am endeavouring to track your journey as you hurtle down the river that black November night, and understand why it was nearly seven miles 'on' before your body came to rest.

Just above the spot where the drama began, Jackie plants a memorial for you, a native hedge rose, a guelder, a genus – viburnum, Latin, 'the wayfaring tree' – related to the honeysuckle, with white flowers followed by red leaves and berries in the autumn. She adds snowdrops and is going to put in some primroses and daffodils as well.

Here it is that I start my trek after you.

I continue to marvel at the deceptive sweetness of this water. Where your car went in, right now it's only a few feet wide and, even though it is winter still and there's been rain, I could wade across and the river would only come up to my thighs.

The literature on the valley doesn't prevaricate. 'Although it is likely to be pastoral tranquility when we visit, the weather can be wild here' – and we learn how, in the distant past, seven people were killed when an avalanche of water and rocks hit them, and two more drowned in a flood that washed away bridges. The twelve-and-a-half-mile waterway has been sufficiently powerful to carve out cave systems beneath it. Long years back, Tony Middleton told me, nearly two dozen schoolchildren and teachers were trapped on a ledge in a cave at the head of the valley and the water rose to within eighteen inches of them, but then levelled off. Had they been caught in the water they could have disappeared forever into the honeycomb of subterranean holes below and around the river.

Today, gurgling like a baby, the river slides north-westwards through an avenue of bare trees on crumbling flanks. The water is slow and even, black in colour with pewter lights. To the left, other side of the river from her home, rises Jackie's privately purchased moor, beetling crags cuffed by clouds, withholding all invitation. Down here the cold grey day is redeemed by massed ranks of snowdrop.

The shingle ridge on which your car foundered about three-quarters of a mile down has little water percolating through it; the river divides on either side. With waders you could make a crossing on foot even here. The blue rope used to tether the wreck to a branch still dangles from it. I see where they've buzz-sawed shrubbery back so they could drag the waterlogged motor up the bank. The ground's churned. Suddenly, as I stand there, the sun bursts through milling cloud. It blazes for less than two minutes, and then is gone. It's the only time the sun shines, unexpurgated, all day.

You 'around', France?

In all this seven-mile madness not a bone in your body was broken. You rode the rapids like an inflatable, and I guess that the point you hit something really hard was not until you came to a place appropriately called Rash, a dark one-horse hamlet where the river starts to engage in a robust tangle with reefs a little less than halfway through your misfortune. The skull may have suffered its more serious wounds even farther on, where the water piles into a ravine with edges. Ouch, Ruth. Dear Ruth, rag doll in the flood.

Where river number one joins river number two there's a dark pool that would have terrified you at any time but, in the summer, had me jumping in with glee. I eat my sandwich there. I watch myself wanting you to come bowling down river one so I can scoop you out and save you from river two, which is a rather more serious business.

Why you've not snagged up somewhere before now seems bizarre. There have been enough boulders, upended trees, dipping branches, islands, shelves, clefts, holes and side-waters to have detained any number of bodies, dead or alive. The entire river has impaled on its woodwork a huge and depressing swathe of litter, the tin, plastic and sisal crap of those 'custodians of the country-side', the farmers. But no, there was no holding you. You raced down the river like you drove on the roads.

After three-and-a-half hours I come to the end of your journey. It would have taken you thirty minutes. I sit under the great, bare oak tree where your friends Anne Waters and Liz Ashbourne found your name, 'Ruth', spelled out, the 'R' three feet high, in woven leaves on the grass four days after you'd been located, dead, the other side of the water. Anne was walking on her own, a little apart from her companion, when she was summoned to 'come and look at what's here.' Said Anne, 'I turned back and there it was at the side: such a moving tribute, the naturalness of it all and the vibrancy of the autumn colours in the "Ruth" – what an occasion for the pair of us . . . overwhelmingly emotional.' To this day neither Anne nor anyone else we know has any idea who did this. Anne thinks it might have been the rescue people.

Anyway, just another mystery to leave behind with the rest.

Crossing the bridge ahead, I seek out your final resting place; the exact spot. *Why here*? I wonder, still. There's no clear answer. The river has at this point in its proceedings done fierce right then left turns in very quick succession and may have flung you up where it did as it careered round the second corner on two wheels almost. Perhaps it was simply a case of the spate abating, the level of the water dropping and gently marooning you. Had you gone on another four hundred yards round a bend of ninety degrees you'd have ended up in river number three and perhaps been lost to us forever, disappearing without trace out to sea; leaving us with no clear idea what might have happened to you. At least we have had the body to mourn and lay roses on.

The police officer who coordinated the rescue effort meets to show me where they'd found you. He said the rescuers themselves had been amazed how far you had travelled. On a high bank over the pebble wash PC Shaun Downing guides my eyeline to a rock on its own, about five feet square, immediately below us. Downing said you were spreadeagled, face down, across it, your lower body in a few inches of water, head and shoulders out. There was a deep rent across the right side of your head and you were badly bruised all over. You lay in your underthings only. Had the rest of your clothing been ripped from you by the force of the water or had you freed yourself from the heavy garments to try to stop yourself sinking? Did you put up a hell of a struggle, then, in that turbulent flood? Might all that repressed anger have got you, in a valuable way (potentially, at least), fighting mad at last? We'll never know, will we?

The place where your journey ended here at the river's edge is, again in your life, 'in the middle of nowhere'. There's no village, hamlet, nothing except a holiday bungalow standing empty to one side. There's a wood on a rise in front of you, earth cliff to your right; on the opposite bank, to your left, the great old oak with arms outstretched as if to welcome you back to nature. Behind you, on the bend you've just shot round, sheep feed on landslip. Bare hills hint in the distance. It's very peaceful.

Job done, the policeman takes his leave. Alone, I climb down to the rock where you'd lain and squat before it. It's an unexceptional grey slab with mottled green and orange flecks, striated, sharp. Above, in the shrubs, little wings swoop and twitter. Down here the river is loud. I straddle the rock itself trying even now to feel, be with you, not to have you gone. Yet I do not weep. I do not feel. I'm empty; dead myself. Grieving's early shock, denial, lamenting – rage – have given way to dull depression. I am a nought, cold as the winter air around me.

Feels like you're starting to leave me, slowly. No more white owls, clairvoyant whispers, Ruth France doubles, identical hand-writings, callings out in dreams and ghostings and, not least, writing carried high on thermals. Reality has become little daily chippings with words, a pale man hunched on a rock, and no more contact from France at all.

That earlier burst of sunshine today over the exact spot where you'd drowned?

Nah.

WELL, JACKIE BELIEVES you did not die in vain. That your death might even be seen as *good*. That's what you liked about Jackie, she wasn't in the least bit conventional, or sentimental. Your friend and protector studied and practised shamanism with the Bushmen of the Kalahari and had a rich and spirited interior life all her own.

Those last ten exceptional months of your life, from seeing the lama, 14 January, to your death, 11 November, Jackie believes you became 'enlightened' – or got somewhere close. She told me, 'I think Ruth had finally got to her destination. She found what she'd been searching for, all these years.'

Which was?

'Freedom. The last I saw her she was taking me to catch a train at the station. I was going back to America. I'd never seen her more radiant. I asked her, what was *happening* to her? She said, "I've never felt such freedom." I'm sure of it; Ruth had got to the place she wanted to get to. *She was a different person.*'

How did Jackie interpret the word 'freedom' here? 'When you've nothing left to lose.' She added, 'I believe it was Ruth's right time to go. In that sense her death was "good". She died while still *alive*, she hadn't *died in life* as so many do and as she'd threatened to do herself, on more than one occasion.'

Your friend was unflinching. 'I'm *glad*, therefore, Ruth's gone as and when she has.'

Jackie I barely knew despite each of us having been so close to you. We lived in different worlds. The few times we'd met I'd found her attractive, a weathered mountain woman, because of her plain dealings and being as solidly earthed as she was; at the same time, the downside, I thought she came across as a little forbidding sometimes. Distant, even. I think she warmed herself at your 'fire' while you anchored yourself in her 'ground'. What did she find so special about your friendship? 'Similar values, though we were very different people. I don't know why our friendship happened like it did. No idea. But it was a spiritual thing, definitely.'

She went on: 'Ruth, Sara and the cats Indy and Minou – all four were wounded animals; Ruth with her broken life, Sara from a dogs' home and a horribly abused past, and the cats just out of the trauma of six months' quarantine after I'd brought them over from the States, where I'd been living. I used to watch them on the couch together, all four of them, and it was always about *healing*. Four fractured souls bonding together; a delight to watch. Sara would always sit with Ruth even when I was there. She adored Ruth and their lives, and ultimately deaths, were so totally intertwined. When Ruth was coming up the drive in her car Sara would know it was her instinctively and shoot out to greet her. Between them, joy was the big word. And peace.'

Jackie told the tale of a young boy under your care in social services. He'd been very troubled, a nightmare for you to 'hold' and to help. Once, you took him for a ride in your car with Sara in the back. The boy turned with a sour expression on his face and said to the two of you, 'I don't like dogs.'

'Sara licked him on the face and the boy melted. It was the first time, apparently, he'd ever been "kissed" in his life. He came to worship the dog and would throw sticks for her all day long. It was Sara's unconditional affection that changed the child. He went into a foster home and Ruth told me he did OK.'

Jackie's observations as to the genesis of your later depressions tie in with my own; in your not having had a fixed place to live for so long, and not knowing what to do with your life as the years went by. 'Ruth had a real fear of growing old. There was a lot of insecurity,' she reflects. 'Then, Eureka – the remarkable change at the end.'

What did Jackie prize most about you? No contest: your honesty in looking at yourself and admitting your failings. 'Ruth knew her life, her behaviour, they weren't right. Why couldn't she deal better with it all? Why was she so emotional? I think it was because she so wanted to be the best she could be. Hence her huge, undying struggle.'

Classic example, indeed, of what my counselling preceptor Carl Rogers called 'the actualising tendency', 'the directional trend evident in all organic and human life; the urge to expand, extend, develop, mature – the tendency to express and activate all the capacities of the organism, or the self.'

An impulse you'd manifested, France, with all your heart. Your big, big heart.

THE JOY and clear interior skies of that last unparalleled year together have clouded over, after all; I wasn't flying as high as I'd thought. Week by week you're fading badly, leaving me with twinges still, I'm 'being abandoned'. There are lessons to be learned yet in the arts of letting go. As ever, hook or by crook, I try to hang on to the loved one; forlorn, I go stay with Chris in London, and we talk hours on end about his mother. I think though Chris found it healing too.

Your lifelong apprehensions 'around' the wet stuff: 'When Rob and I were kids,' Chris said, 'and we were all away on holiday, Mum always used to make the excuse "I don't like getting my hair wet" whenever we tried to get her to join us in the water. Back home, she didn't even like *taking* us to the swimming baths never mind going in, which she never did.'

How did he see you, generally? 'She was always so very emotional, always enthusiastic *about* emotions, and I was the rational one. She was frustratingly liberal, with Rob say smoking weed in the back garden with all his mates and Mum reckoning it was perfectly all right and me thinking, "*No, it's not.*"

'I don't remember her, ever, shouting at me. She just didn't do angry. Instead, she'd over-analyse the reasons why people were doing stuff. She was always interested in my and Rob's emotional wellbeing. I remember the school parents' evenings and I think

Mum was the only one in the place who wanted a session with the personal and social development teacher. She wanted to ask, "How *are* the boys?" not "How or what are they doing?" She was very passionate about the two of us, and our being happy.

'She first got depressed after Rob was born. Then the time she and Dad were starting to split I knew something was going on, things weren't OK, and I'd walk into a room and find my mum crying. She made excuses saying it was "to do with the car" or something. I knew it wasn't.'

Why were his parents growing apart? 'Mum said, "We started to drift that way. I began to get interested in meditation and enlightenment" – her own pathology – "but your dad was working towards retirement and wasn't interested in meditation or anything like that, and we just had different priorities." '

Chris corroborated Jackie's underlining your honesty in looking at yourself but felt you overdid it. 'Mum would insist, "I need to tell Tricia how I feel," for example, but Tricia didn't necessarily want to know how Mum felt at that point. Mum used to be very insistent about things sometimes, didn't always exercise social responsibility, a bit of sensitivity to the needs and wishes of others who might not want to be so expansive about their feelings, or anything else.

'After Dad left, the money troubles started. Mum was on income support and felt dreadful. She went without food, missed meals, just so she had enough to feed Rob and me.'

Then Chris's touching vignette: 'After school I was working in the chip shop in the village, Friday nights and weekends, and I'd bring home a big bar of chocolate and a bottle of cider, stuff like that, as a little treat for her. I really wanted to help her.

'Today there's a big need I have about being able to have and provide the financial security my mum never had; why I'm a corporate sales manager earning pretty handsome money. My mum's generosity used to drive me friggin' nuts with David there and not working. He was a passive kind of guy and the frustration came with my mum working her arse off and him doing nothing.'

Mum's difficulties with anger? 'They could go back to Granddad. If you did something that pissed him off he didn't "do angry" either – but in his case it was rejection, instead. He clammed up and punished you with his silence. I think it was probably that which upset her. But there's nothing I remember like Mum saying, "I am like I am because of how my dad treated me then." I recall lots of happy times with Granddad . . . chasing cabbage whites with nets and me and Rob running naked through the garden sprinklers and lots of rough-and-tumble fun. He was a great granddad.'

Chris is then refreshingly frank about his mother and me, not mincing his words: 'She used to say to us, "*John* gets angry or loses his temper," and she always found it hard when you were in a restaurant and something wasn't right and you had a pop at the service – that sort of thing. I think she found it embarrassing. She always had a very great respect for your books and felt you were a kind of split personality; the meditative writer who preached calm, but then there were elements in your life that didn't fit – with your getting cross with someone simply serving you dinner, say. She was quite protective of you and when you were with us and working she'd ask us to be quiet. "John's writing a book." *She was angry with you* though for the break-up when you decided on that in the end.'

But then came the rather piercing reminder I've a fair bit of work on myself to do yet: 'After you'd got back from Greece this time and I asked Mum how it had all gone, she said she'd had a lovely time "but there were moments it was the usual with John." '

Ouch.

I thought it had been paradise and tranquility all the way.

I go on chasing you elsewhere. Rob, in Kenya, looks back on a 'happy and secure' childhood with you, 'even though my mum always said it wasn't.' *Serious* depression hit you after he'd grown up and gone. 'It took an awful lot out of her. She was wonderful dealing with the problems of others, but not so good at handling problems of her own, always insisting everything was OK. She seemed to have no idea we could see through these white lies. She'd tell me she was going out or had just got back from the cinema and I knew she'd been sitting inside for days on end and not speaking to anyone.'

Rob came up with a poignant, perceptive line that made me laugh: *'I think if I'd rung her up on her mobile while she was trapped in the car and drifting down the river, she would have said, "I'm round at Doug's place, Rob, and we've just sat down to a lovely meal. Can I ring you back tomorrow?"'*

I believed him.

'This,' he admitted, 'was at times infuriating, but I couldn't be cross with her because I knew she was just trying to save me and Chris from worrying. Simply a way she thought she could make us happier, which was her top priority.

'After all the drinking and the ECT, the suicide attempt and the lies, she said to me, once: "Rob, I know I've lost your trust because of what happened, and I know I need to win it back." I said some reassuring things but not what I should have said, which was that she was the person I could trust most in all the world.'

You just about 'gone altogether' now, I, driven, unutterably lonely, press on for the village near England's South Coast where you were brought up. Herstmonceux, its very name asserting its blue-blood Norman links, though in fact a Saxon settlement originally – and what a very pretty and well-shod place it is, hey Ruth? I'd not realised you'd come from such a posh spot. I can quite see why you had always wanted to live your life in the country; the roots of that love affair lie here. But it really is toffee territory, my love. Restaurant dripping with French snobbery, a 'bespoke kitchen' shop, acupuncture clinic, art gallery (rubbish), 'bespoke florist' – and then there it is at last, I've found it, the dwelling where you were born, the old 'semi' cottage with the white wooden face just around the corner from the shops. It's beautiful. When you were there, your cousin Barbara tells me, the two of us at the front gate down memory lane, your mother and father had their little newsagents' business in a wooden extension at the side. In the forties and fifties Herstmonceux wasn't quite the upmarket hub it is today; it was, she said, 'more a farming community', genuinely rustic.

I have tea with Barbara, your other cousin John and his wife Myrtle, and Audrey Harris who was a great friend of your parents. All remember you with so much affection.

'Ooh she was wilful, she knew what she wanted, did Ruth,' Barbara says of your childhood. 'She did like a bit of fun. Was a bit tomboyish.'

'Used to wear her shoes out very quickly,' pops in Audrey, all quirky nugget.

'Nice, homely, friendly girl,' John reckons.

Barbara: 'We envied Ruth and Alf and Ethel's other children because they all had such a lovely childhood. They were always beautifully dressed. Their dad was a kind, loving person but he had his times when he had a black depression and he couldn't help it. He'd been treated cruelly as a child on a farm he'd been packed off to, to work. He lived in. His brother came off even worse; he ended up in prison.'

Your cousin backed up Chris's observation that your father did have a tendency to shut down, go cold on people if they crossed him. 'It was because of how he'd been forced to survive as a kid.' Yes, John said, your father could be 'hard work' sometimes.

Your mother? They all thought the world of her. She was 'like Ruth, very warm and giving'.

Barbara, the one who wrote in the remembrances about your

rising high on a swing to get a glimpse of 'a builder next door', said his name was Roy. He was the son of the builder, helping his father. And your enterprise on the swing had paid off. It was Roy who became that exemplary first lover you'd had when you were just fourteen.

You were terrified that your father would find out. One day he and your mother were walking down the road and you and Roy were walking up, and there was no way you could avoid them. Panic stations. Your parents went past, your father merely offering a clipped 'Afternoon' as though you and your lover were total strangers. I wonder what happened after that. Whatever, I bet you didn't sleep a lot that night.

Clear where your wiles with money came from, heaps of credit cards and jiggery-pokery at the end: your mother. Once she borrowed some dosh from nephew John and promised to pay him back 'threefold'. Your cousin thought that wasn't too bad an investment *at all*, hey? Eventually your mother presented John with a cheque – folded in three.

As for your Romany inheritance, yes it was there in the family and your gran, your father's mother, used to earn money selling sprigs of 'lucky butcher's broom', the yellow flowers interwoven with others made by her with painted wax, round where she lived. I told my hosts how I used to call you 'Gipsy'. They liked that.

Then your family moved down into Bexhill-on-Sea, about ten miles away, as you entered your teens. Your father's light haulage business (set up with others in the family) that had followed on from the newsagents' had crashed in a nasty domestic fall-out. Your parents went back to shopkeeping. This time it was a paper shop that sold general stuff as well.

It's a cold winter's night as I venture into the town to discover where you'd been: the shop of yore is Easy Tan, a tanning salon, today. It's in a shopping street. The two storeys of living quarters above the business are featureless and faded. A West Ham football flag hangs dustily in one window. There's a Sky dish. I can't picture you here *whatsoever*. After the sweet shingled cottage in Herstmonceux it all looks a terrible disappointment.

I walk the streets and am almost alone. Bexhill is populated especially by the elderly, retiring by a sea scratching at mudbank and stones. I eat in an Italian restaurant on the front, ending up the only customer, listening to the synapses firing in my brain. It is England at its dreariest. Not ghastly, just ordinary; nothing to get excited, or upset, about at all. I suspect the scarlet-frocked Carmen would have had a little bit of a problem finding her place here. You tried to liven things up, I'm told, by mischieving at Bexhill Grammar. But I remember your talking about the town with shrugged indifference. You really did fear ending up in a care home in a hole like this, as your widowed mother did, quietly giving up on the world and wetting your knickers.

But where you are laid to rest, my love – here is somewhere special. In the ancient churchyard of All Saints in Herstmonceux, the church an unusual confection of redbrick, plaster and stone with a stubby tower and timbered steeple some distance from the heart of the village, down a long and winding lane, I come to the single grave where you lie on top of your mother who, in turn, is laid upon your father. On the simplest of stones are written the words 'In fond remembrance of Alfred Tidy, August 1910 – April 1986 and Ethel May Tidy, May 1917 – March 2004', concluding with: 'In the garden of memory we meet every day'.

Your ashes, in a biodegradable vessel, have been laid in the earth immediately below the turf close to the headstone. A small stone marking *your* life and death is going to be laid horizontally on this spot.

On your grave now? Just a small clump of washed-out plastic flowers and the remains, stalks, of some tiny posy; real.

There are several other members of your family laid up here, including brother Alan, the RAF man who died of cancer aged only thirty-two. This sibling you *had* got on with. Famously. He'd been the apple of your eye.

This is England sublime. Behind the church, the mighty fifteenth-century, barleycorn-chimneyed and peppermill-turreted Herstmonceux Castle, immaculate in renovation in its imposing lake; one of the finest brick buildings in Britain, in whose grounds once stood one of the royal observatories. The castle is now an international study centre. And in front of us – well, Ruth, this was the view you had always said was one of your most treasured. The panorama is vast; it extends mile upon mile across marshland, the Pevensey Levels, with the subtle Downs creeping in to the left. Woman of spacious vision that you were, for all your flaws, this the perfect place, yes, for you to end your days, gazing out upon endless light.

I sit beside you on the mound and place my hand on you, as though I might be giving you healing. The sun breaks palely through mackerel sky at my shoulder, and everywhere is so much at peace. It's the country of rooks and big skies, the ancient Anderida of the Romans ending in Beachy Head, the 'Beau Chef' or geological handsome boss of William the Conqueror's time. I could sit here a long time listening to the silence.

Meanwhile the frozen wastes of the past weeks are melting in the faint sunshine and I am so close to you here, closer in the flesh than we have ever been since our farewell hug that last, glad afternoon on the fell three months before, and the tears roll into the grass as though you have only at this moment gone.

It is so appropriate; the hymned voices of your great love, the children, rise in a special service for them this Sunday morning from the church.

I'm alive. So alive. I've found you again, right here at home.

BUT NOW IT'S THE INQUEST into your death, and the day is as cold and dark and miserable as that was. The relentless grisliness of England's weather is taking its toll. I am longing to be back with you on the sun-splashed isle in Greece, what feels like lifetimes away.

Anne Waters comes with me to the colourless courtroom in the county town. When I start to give my evidence I find it difficult to talk through the tears. I rally and, very briefly, tell the hearing about your last few hours on earth. That's all.

The coroner announces that you drowned and there were no medical or other conditions contributing to your death. 'Neither alcohol nor drugs were involved.' The postmortem report says your scalp had a deep laceration on the right side in the temporal region, and another at the top. These gashes went down to the bone. There was extensive bruising on the right of your forehead and some multiple smaller bruises on the face, particularly around the right eye. Bangs, too, to thighs, hands, trunk and arm. The long bones, pelvis, vertebral column, skull and ribs all appeared intact. There were no significant internal injuries at all.

Police accident investigator Anthony Foy says your old Ford had no mechanical defects. It was in neutral gear when found, suggesting you'd not had enough time to get into reverse and back out of the flood. Then, 'The engine had breathed in water through the air-intake system and that caused the engine to stop. There was no likelihood of re-starting it.' When the car was discovered snagged on the stones that kilometre downstream, your window was down. Because the vehicle had been swung round to face upriver, there was little hope of your being able to open doors to exit; the force of the water against them would have been too great. So PC Foy was convinced you did get out through the window. At that point, on the shingles, the water was halfway up the windscreen.

And as he's telling us this I think, in that case you could have clambered on the roof maybe, or sat on the window ledge with your legs in the car and clung to the doorframe with your fingers. Rescuers, firemen joining the Middleton brothers, would then have been with you within minutes. You could well be alive, today.

As for your state of mind apropos the weather and the water on the road, coroner Ian Smith, summing up, said, 'It was dark and I suspect she just didn't think about it.' He went on: 'I am satisfied completely that what she tried to do, although it was a misjudgement, was get out of the car through the window. It is possible she tried to get onto the roof and had fallen into the water. It is also possible that she had tried to wade to the bank from the car but whatever she did try to do, sadly it was to no effect because I am sure she was swept away very quickly by the force of the water.' His verdict: accidental death.

Nevertheless, knowing your terror of 'deep, dark water where I can't see the bottom', my belief is you fled before you ever got to the shingles. You didn't know there was the possible 'life-saver' of the raised stones ahead, did you? I suspect that once you realised you were afloat and had shot under the bridge, you opened your window pronto to get the hell out of there, shipped some water through that, tried to save Sara, saw there wasn't anything more you could do for her inert form in the frothing pool in the rear, squeezed through the gap, and dropped into the void.

The coroner isn't very happy that nothing has been done to prevent further accidents at the spot. There was a meeting of councillors on the riverside the day after you died, but nearly half a year later there'd been no announcement about safety measures. The coroner said, 'The water can't be kept off the road, I don't think, but the effects of the water can be minimised in some way. When things can be done that can save lives they should be done, and so that's the reason I am going to write to the highways authority.'

The very next day the county council announced that a twenty-two-metre timber and steel barrier was going to be installed on Flood Lane, across the fatal 'gap', the following month. For twenty years people in cars had been getting trapped in floods at the spot where you died and it took twenty years for the council to do something. *Act.* Yours was the first death there. Who can be made accountable? No one. But your death wasn't just an accident; it was an avoidable tragedy.

The next day, too, I speak to the police again and discover that the following had been recovered from the river around the time you were found: one sock, a Wellington boot, scarf, and your wallet.

Remains of a life, hey?

IT'S APRIL, Easter in Greece, and here I am back on Levitka just six months after we left her, together. And life in the slow lane isn't altogether vanquished; it has taken me three days to get here. Three days to the Aegean merely, Ruth. The North to London and Athens: one day. Day two: fly to the main island. Day three: boat to little Levitka. The joys of travel out of season. A superlative crawl.

I arrived in the evening. The sun was radiant and Stepanos the old-world gentleman from our little guest house is at the quay to meet me. I'd written to him about everything and asked that I might stay in your old room. On our arrival at the pension he and his wife invited me to their leafy patio for coffee and a titbit, Joanna's home-stewed, home-grown grapes in syrup. After that, well, you were clear about that one: straightaway back to the *kafeneio* for ouzo and lemon, and watching the world go by, fat smile on one's face. The little old lady who owned the place was there still and, via a girl interpreting, I told her what had happened to you and why I was back. She knew me right away, I could tell by her smile. She came and sat by me on the street for a while on her own, and in Greek offered her commiserations for your death. I didn't understand a word and at the same time understood every one. In English I thanked her for her kindness. She understood that too. She told me, in Greek and gestures, that she and Stepanos are related. Perhaps she'd known then of your death already. Small world, Levitka.

So I sit here in the watercolour end-of-day sunshine and there you are, other side of the little Cycladean-blue table, smacking the ouzo around the mouth with relish. On cue, the same cheerful guy passes by, '*kalispera*', all, on his ass. For my part never has a man scratched 'Wish you were here' more fervently on paper, this soft April evening in Greece made specially for France.

I stay up till midnight. It's Easter Saturday and on the stroke of twelve Greece goes berserk. Levitka turns out en masse to celebrate the new day's Resurrection. Venue: the marble courtyard outside the church. Everyone in best bib and tucker, tapers aloft. Such handsome young men and women, though they could be from anywhere in the world judging by their dress. Global bloody designer chic, gals dolled up like high-price whores, jabbering into their mobiles while the priest belts out his office and whirls his smoke. He's that choleric-faced little chap to whom you took some concerned dislike. At one point he snaps at a kid who's in his way, then barks at the bell-ringer for playing the damn bells too enthusiastically (above the din the cleric can't make himself heard).

The general racket is augmented however by firecrackers going off in the warren of tiny streets around. I've never heard bangers like them; it all felt like an artillery shelling. I kept jumping like a startled frog. Then came the sacramental exchanges of *mwahs* on both cheeks and there is no one to kiss me and no one to kiss in return so I just stand there as Eternal Observer, the Writer, looking a bit square peg in round hole. I experience no whiff of Easter glory – I let go my Christian beliefs so many lifetimes ago – but I envy the powerful sense of community here, a people bonded in an Orthodoxy perhaps, in the scale of things, delivering more good than harm. Everyone looks pleased to be here, anyway. Happy, even. And I am happy for them. But the edge of my solitary state is sharpened. I think I'm the only foreigner here.

When I get back to your room, before I turn in I sit a while with the wreath of *fila dafnis* ('leaves of glory') I'd asked a florist on the main island to make for you, and brought over with me on the boat. I'm going to weave a galaxy of wild flowers into the leaves then send the lot out to sea in remembrance of you and because you loved this place with such passion.

My first full day I have to get in my first wild swim of the year. April 19 only. Unheard of! The water, refreshing. I was trekking around the western and northern shores of the island and dropping down the east coast but tiring fast, so I went and plunged naked into the sea. It was proving one of the most difficult walks I think I'd undertaken anywhere, ever. The terrain was unrelentingly hostile; flinty, riddled with thorn and thistle, snagged further with endless chines, steep rises and vertiginous walls, and sometimes rendered nigh impassable, even, due to the density of shrub. Hour after hour I reeled, stumbled and fell, seven in all. I'd hoped to walk the shoreline of the whole island in a day but, by the time exhaustion had set in and my flesh was torn to shreds, I'd only covered half. The venture, I think, was sort of a trying to claim the island as 'ours', like a dog marking territory with its leg-overs. My marking was blood, sweat and curses; on Easter Sunday, alas, far too many loud offerings of 'Jesus-effin'-Christ'.

As intemperate, I can be, as yon priest? (France across the way, nodding.)

The writer Hermann Hesse, one of my favourite in my younger

days, wrote that patience 'is the most difficult and the only thing which is worth learning.' He said that all nature, all growing, all peace and all beauty are based on patience. 'They need time, need silence, need trust, need the belief in the long-term processes of a much longer period than a single life.' So, alright, there are some things I do expressly 'believe'.

Patience: still, am I not, a work-in-progress?

Day two, I ambled up to the main café, in the square, and had a breakfast omelette of bacon, mushrooms and peppers, with coffee. I bought sardines, baked sesame rolls and two bananas for tea. Then I sit here the day long in my open French windows overlooking the rise of giant daisies and poppies, and the bright blue sea beyond. The quiet is extraordinary; it plays jazz in the ears, accompanied by singing birds, the hummed threads of an occasional bee. The gauze curtains at the side, the cloth on my writing table, shuffle in the breeze. I have absolutely nothing to do, again, but be with you.

I feel your presence now *more* than at any time since you died. Yesterday on my expedition, time and again, I thought I heard noises off – stones chinking, brushwood breaking, shrubs swishing – that made me stop, amazed, thinking it must be you alongside, just that fraction behind as used to be the case as 'the impatient Pepper' pressed on, the life long, towards his retreating horizons. Once, I stopped and called out 'Are you there, then?' The response, pure France: 'Of course I bloody well am!'

Probably making all of it up, still, every thought and whisper, because I just long to be with you. I love you so much.

THE NOVELIST Jeanette Winterson wrote: 'Nothing could be more familiar than love. Nothing else eludes us so completely. My search for you, your search for me, goes beyond life and death into one long call into the wilderness. I do not know if what I hear is an answer or an echo. Perhaps I will hear nothing. It doesn't matter. The journey must be made.'

I think my letter here is that 'one long call into the wilderness'. My 'journey'.

What I do know is that the love I bear you now is born of all that's the best in me and not, as was once the case in my love lives with others, and for no little time with you, the worst. I do not need you any more, nor indeed anyone, to make me happy. I can sit here on my Greek hillside without you, save in memory, in peace; can let your earthly fabric go. All feels a terrible sadness that is also vaulting joy.

I head off and explore the bits of the island I've 'missed', where the wild flowers dance and dazzle coast to coast. I get down to a new beach (only soul there) and lie under a tree and read. There's a party going on in a villa up the road, dispensing that Greek pop pap that sounds like someone having their entrails sucked out by the island cesspit truck then sliced into thin strips with rusting bouzouki strings. Normally I'd be railing the rape of the silence but I'm in good nick, I shrug, read a couple of chapters, and doze instead to the music of the sea at my feet. Would I prefer to be having a ball up on the terrace there? No I wouldn't. What is 'society' anyway? Thomas Merton, the monk, described it as 'the pretentious routines of a disordered togetherness'. Nice. But sad. No, in nothing I have all I need. And on the way home, guess what? A rock falls off a wall as I pass. An abandoned, battered JCB by the roadside lets out a loud metallic *boing*. Real events.

He–llooooo?

Eckhart, mystic, several centuries back, said that it is only when we are content with having and being nothing that 'the mind clamours for the highest good of all.' The highest good? Beyond the confusions, losses, doubts, debt, drink, your expanding flesh, the silent wrath of your father, David Cole, the hard time you had at work, the loneliness of your years on the road, your apprehensions around ageing, then death, and the godawful driving that drove you straight into its jaws – you lived a life, Ruth, which could be summed up in one word: *service*. Is there any calling higher? Isn't it the word that's 'Open Sesame!' to all wisdom, truth and joy, some would say the royal road to God? OK, you and I would simply murmur, 'Peace'. I reckon you did: you sought and found 'the highest good'.

And perhaps the amazed Tony Middleton, last person on earth to see you alive, was not wrong, that as you dashed towards what your heart must have been telling you now, so urgently, lay ahead of you, your demise, you *were* 'calm', that, hosannas, at the last – some lesson – you did let go all your fears from the past and flowed to your death 'enlightened', at rest. If there is another life for you after this one, could it be one where you will have finally conquered your terror of drowning, your many anxieties, and die the next time quietly in bed, with your cocoa?

'To affect the quality of the day, that is the highest of the arts,' Thoreau believed. And you did just that for virtually everyone with whom you came into contact; you 'made their day'. You used to bemoan the fact (a bit) that you weren't an artist. Why you put me on something of a pedestal because I *was*. Yet you lived your life 'growing up into the fullness of it,' as someone wrote recently in my newspaper, 'when we learn to take responsibility for love's fortunes in a fallen world.' As a practitioner in the art of loving, France, you were an artist supreme.

So, how must *I* be here on in the last days in order to love in life and die in peace; join you one day, I hope, the dust shaken from one's feet, in a quiet *kafeneio* up someplace among the stars? Literature offers few directions. The gods and goddesses were falling out from the start, liaisons marked by war and rape and general ill temper. The great mortal love stories (say, for example,

Antony and Cleopatra, Tristan and Isolde, Abelard and Heloïse, Romeo and Juliet, Burton and Taylor) are all either ruinous, or jokes. Where the narratives are more realistic they're a relentless grainy indictment of the whole sorry business of 'love'; take novels, or the TV soaps night after night. Even 'loving our neighbour' today invites scorn; 'kindness a virtue of losers' as one literary figure mourned recently, and our social fabric a wasteland of selfishness, greed and despair. 'Work harder' the salvation, our masters cry, when the truth would seem to be that laziness is the one divine fragment of godlike existence left to us from paradise. (Fragment from my notebooks: 'When a niece of his joyfully told him how her husband had at last found a job, Uncle Bertie replied: "Oh, my dear, I'm so sorry." ')

Conventional religion? Spare me.

No, everywhere I look there are no readily accessible guides to 'the good life', 'the highest good', which invite freedom of spirit as co-creator along the way. No independence that is married to community. No soaring new love between man and woman, or same-sex, pointing to the possibility of a better world. Ruth, as you did I hope at the last, as, sensibly, we all have to when our time comes, knowing not one whit what lies ahead, we have to make our peace, if such be our desire, with *nothing*. I now understand, fully, the mystic's smile that says 'Not this', 'Not that'. And what is meant when William Blake enjoined us: 'Go, love without the help of anything on earth.'

I begin to draw to a close. The weather changes, and violent winds batter the island. They scream at the seams of windows and doors, and the flowers that have been quietly rotating on their axles to keep their faces to the sun – watching them hour after hour, day after day as they turn has been one long meditation – are now blown to bits, seeming to reel across the fields like drunks. There are dust devils in the streets and the sea is roaring. Little children are blown about as brightly coloured balloons. The men have all retreated to the clatter of their *tavli* (backgammon) boards in the bowels of the caff.

I sit remembering my father with much fondness. For it was he who set me off on my passion for wandering the world, putting me on a train at the station when I was aged a mere thirteen and having the courage and confidence to let me travel all the way to Hamburg on my own to see my new German penfriend, Gerold Brandis, as our two countries tried to heal after a war which had had Sergeant Pepper fighting all the way through Europe to – Hamburg. That waving me off to Germany had been an attempt by him to live by love. The odyssey in search of same that's consumed my life, I owe to my dad.

The gale has gone. Light and warmth return. The majesty of flowers, green hills, stone walls, and clouds gently floating about the place and keeping us watered and alive is contained in the frame of the French windows here at my table. Two birds are singing a love duet out there. A distant child calls. The breeze strolls and sings. 'Stillness is the mother of wisdom,' indeed.

'Out of non-doing comes meaningful activity. Such an experience acts as the springboard for wise engagement with the world' – the clipping catching my eye at my side. Remembrance of the words of Ramakrishna, that so long as the bee is outside the petals of the lotus and has not tasted the honey, it hovers around the flower, buzzing noisily. But when it is inside the flower it drinks the nectar silently, and is still.

I'll go up the lane to the caff, and tidy up today's lines to you. You'll come with me? Great. Sweet time when joy is spicy sausage toast and camomile tea with a ghost in the village square far away from home and the familiar, under the nourishing sun of our enchanted Greece.

This moment now, the kingdom, Ruth. And we need ever nothing more.

LAST DAY ON LEVITKA. Dawn broke on the back of the old north wind that has that bit of a bite to it. Good news. 'Our' beach, Telmadi I'll call her, is south-facing, so the *meltemi* will take your wreath straight out to – well, wherever. Africa I'd like to hope.

I'd made sure I got a good stout construction. I wanted to give the wreath a fighting chance of at least a few days at sea. Remember Despina Kitini, the leggy blonde of uncertain years with the gaze of an eagle? She ran the info centre on the main island, among other businesses, and helped us so much. Gorgeous glad spirit; she and I have kept in touch. (*No*, Ruth, she's married. Just very kind and, deliciously, a little bit wild.) She went with me to the florist's to make sure I got exactly what I wanted. Going to get you to Egypt or Libya if I can. More sun, empty beaches and silence. More 'nothing'. You'll more likely be cut to pieces though by a jetski just around the headland from Telmadi. Or the wind will change and you'll end up in barking mad Athens. God help you.

Soft, last day reflection: I have no one now who can come to Greece with me again. My five longest-standing friends, friend-ships each counting forty years and more, have lately died with you. Six down, three to go; and those three remaining comrades, female, are all in one way or another invalided, unable to strike out for wild, remote places with me. That family of friends, my 'refuge', begins to crumble, go the way of all things too. And you know, even if you hadn't died, I don't think you'd have been 'around' for much longer either. I'd have still been on my own. I doubt you would have married me in the end.

I suspect that once you'd got to Kenya you would have stayed there. Rob said the boarding school where he teaches cries out for houseparents. You'd have got a job, no problem. Then there was the orphanage to which you'd be drawn too; possibly (all your experience and gifts) ending up running the place. And above all you'd have had your son and Rachel and granddaughter back with you; a whole new life to build and sustain you, maybe, through to the end. Exciting. Last but not least, there was that superlative African mountain sunshine. The wildlife – Rob: 'I looked out this morning and there was a lion on the golf course' – no, I think you'd have gone. In truth, your passing possibly spared both of us further entanglement and unhappy parting.

But we did, we had a good innings.

Talking of the orphanage, the £1,700 raised at your funeral has fed the children and many more in the village beyond for a month, and enabled a playroom and playground to be built in memory of you. Rob supervised things. The absolutely perfect 'ending', for you.

My final morning and I while it away practising what the guide-book says is 'the art of Greek islands: to learn how to do nothing'. I think I am becoming seriously proficient.

Then, noonday, Stepanos lets me raid his switchback garden for the wild flowers for your wreath. I squat in the dust in the sun and weave gorgeous colour into the two-tone green of the foliage spun on a frame.

There are poppies the dark blood of arteries. The white or yellow ox-eye, *margarita*, size of an old half-crown. Purplish elf-hats called *molocha*. Bellflowers, *kampanaki*, so delicate they threaten to shrivel with one's touch. What are often the first flowers of springtime on these islands, little golden flutes, *xinithra*. Other tiny blooms I can't find names for. I've brought garden ties from England and make certain my handiwork's secure. In the wreath's centre I fix a hand-written card. No fuss: 'Ruth, with my love forever'.

It was important, I think, that the flowers were wild ones, com-plementing the secret wildness of your spirit, that which (I'd come to realise on Levitka) would probably have prevented your ever, finally, committing to me, David or to anyone; your deep-heart's longing to be free.

Telmadi is deserted. I strip and head into the sea. The water's *cold* this time. The wind's a pest, swirling in a circle in the bay and coming *in* off the ocean. Drat. I think about Plan B, getting out and going back up the island to a beach with the wind blowing 'out'. But, just like the wind, I can't make up my mind. Stepanos had insisted the overriding wind today would be the *meltemi*, hadn't he?

I start swimming, pushing the wreath forward with my fingers. The flowers smell of honey. When I pause it seems the wreath snags back the way I've come. I keep going. Prodding, driving south towards the sun. There's not a vessel visible on any horizon. Islands large and small hang mute in the haze.

I swim on. The bloody wreath – Ach! There you go. The *impatience*, brother! – doesn't want to travel, does it? I am starting to feel the cold. Torpor takes over. I recognise there is that in me that is, admit it, sometimes tired-of-life. 'Done it all, been to hell and back, and there can now be nothing new under the sun,' etcetera. Why not let the cold take me, so I fade into silence?

Join you. 'He drowned, too.'

The wreath has to be kept being poked. I can't go back, and the water really is starting to be bitter. I seem a long way out. Half a mile? I've been working thirty-six years as a freelance, with little regular income in all that time, and finally been ground down a bit with – struggle? Would really like to rest. Could stop now, float a while, slip under.

But, suddenly, there's a ratchet change in the wind and I tread water and watch, relieved, delighted, as the wreath starts to motor away from me, out towards the south, the open sea. Out beyond the bay here, the *meltemi*'s doing its job.

As swiftly as you are leaving me, I'm starting to break up. The months of mourning rise to their peak. I'm sobbing like a child in the middle of the Aegean. I want to swim after the wreath – never, ever, let you go. Yet it's travelling too fast. I could never catch it. I thrash around in miserable go-nowhere orbits, torn between chase and (I'm so frozen by this point) heading back to land.

'I miss you so much!' I bellow at the retreating flowers. Involuntarily I duck in my distress and take in a mouthful of water. I cannot bear this. I should've hung the wreath in the tree on the beach under which you loved to sit for hours in your last days in the sun, and I could then have sat there, *hours*, with you.

You are starting to race now. I intercut the images here (you being borne away queenly on a bed of flowers) with those of the night of 11 November when you had no one to see you off, when there were no blossoms or wavings of hands, no cries of 'Bon voyage!' or prancing lights of the sun on deepening Prussian blue waters, no birds wheeling or scent of warm earth and herb, no tiny fishes underworld in darts of silver; indeed, no witnesses, recordings, poems, hope, love or warmth around you, by your side. There was, instead, only a world obliterated in the night and wind and freezing black water of an English winter.

I float on my back, losing sight of you between the freshening waves, then catching you, straining to find you as you disappear once more; up and down and in and out you go.

Shall I live or die? If I let go now, it wouldn't be long before I would know the answer to all mysteries, able, maybe, to make sense of all my days at last. The battle would be over. I'd be at peace? I mean, *serious* peace?

Grief's crazy undertow of phantoms. But then what was the one paragraph in all literature that had done most to sustain me in my half-century of wandering across the world? From Camus' *The Rebel*, one of the books way back that had changed my life, at the close:

'Now is born that strange joy which helps one live and die, and which we shall never again renounce to a later time. On the sorrowing earth it is the unresting thorn, the bitter food, the harsh wind off the sea, the ancient dawn forever renewed. With this joy, through long struggle, we shall remake the soul of our time.'

In the choppy Aegean, 24 April '09, in the end I remembered, and did not betray my calling. There was still so much work, on 'the soul of our time', to be done. And that's what this last letter to you, layer beyond layer, has been all about; love may not 'matter' to my genes, but it matters to me. To that in me that seeks to make life beautiful even if in evolutionary terms it is 'meaningless'. Not that I believe it is. Love understood, and lived, could be springboard to a new world propelling evolution into historic shifts. This one falling apart, comprehensively – was Akong right? – a world I live and shall die for. As you did.

Dangerously perished with cold now, I vow however to be with you until I can see you no longer. I keep looking, through my tears. My last cry? 'I will be patient, Ruth! More than ever, I promise.'

When I focus again, you are gone. I pretend the lights of the sun on the water are the flowers, until I can kid myself no more. Once again you have vanished, waterborne, into the void.

I WANT YOU to know something that's haunted me each day since you died.

For years now I've withheld the words I have wanted to say to you but could not, anticipating that you might never again be able to say them to me in return. I've signed letters with 'my love' and talked about my love for you, and I think made it transparent in a good many of my actions that in some sense language has been unnecessary, perhaps. I've known from your words and hugs that the situation your side seemed much the same. But I couldn't bring myself to utter to your face, straight, the three words in the language that matter most in this life and change things in an instant, and on your death it was with horror I realised that, after your return to

David and my then turning my back on you, I'd not done so once. Not, with a kiss, *spoken* the words. I always held back, wounded by fear – rejection, again.

So I started to write these lines the day after your drowning in order to say to you directly – face-to-face opportunity lost especially, sad to say, in those lovely last days, weeks and months – 'I love you.' Just that.

I also love your children. Much. Be assured, as I was with you, I shall always be here for them.

There, done. My darling somewhere in the wide blue waters of the Aegean, or perhaps here at my side as I draw my letter to a close in the shade of the garden at Despina's tranquil, gracious, unequivocally Cycladean hotel you too loved so much in the main island old town – wherever your journey takes you now, go gently. I'll catch up with you, I pray, one day.

But if there is nothing beyond and you are *gone*, I thank you for the memory of a love that calls to me still through the last twilights of the tinkling bells and piping swifts here on islands far away. In the morning it will be time to move on.

I turned and swam slowly back to the distant shore.

Farewell, Gipsy.

John